S0-BAI-320

THIS BOOK
BELONGS TO:

_____

_____

Animal Encyclopedia Activity Journals

MARINE ANIMALS

MORE THAN 150 PAGES OF MARINE ANIMAL FACTS & FUN ACTIVITIES

JUAN CARLOS ALONSO

Brimming with creative inspiration, how-to projects, and useful information to enrich your everyday life, Quarto Knows is a favorite destination for those pursuing their interests and passions. Visit our site and dig deeper with our books into your area of interest: Quarto Creates, Quarto Cooks, Quarto Homes, Quarto Lives, Quarto Drives, Quarto Explores, Quarto Gifts, or Quarto Kids.

© 2019 Quarto Publishing Group USA Inc.
Artwork © Juan Carlos Alonso
Select images used for design elements and activities © Shutterstock

First published in 2019 by Walter Foster Jr., an imprint of The Quarto Group. 26391 Crown Valley Parkway, Suite 220, Mission Viejo, CA 92691, USA.
T (949) 380-7510 **F** (949) 380-7575 **www.QuartoKnows.com**

All rights reserved. No part of this book may be reproduced in any form without written permission of the copyright owners. All images in this book have been reproduced with the knowledge and prior consent of the artists concerned, and no responsibility is accepted by producer, publisher, or printer for any infringement of copyright or otherwise, arising from the contents of this publication. Every effort has been made to ensure that credits and content accurately comply with information supplied. We apologize for any inaccuracies that may have occurred and will resolve inaccurate or missing information in a subsequent reprinting of the book.

Walter Foster Jr. titles are also available at discount for retail, wholesale, promotional, and bulk purchase. For details, contact the Special Sales Manager by email at specialsales@quarto.com or by mail at The Quarto Group, Attn: Special Sales Manager, 100 Cummings Center, Suite 265D, Beverly, MA 01915, USA.

ISBN: 978-1-60058-852-5

Written and illustrated by Juan Carlos Alonso
Project editing, puzzles, and activities by Elizabeth T. Gilbert

Printed in China
10 9 8 7 6 5 4 3 2 1

For Betty and Dalí, your undying support and endless inspiration make everything worthwhile. Love, Juan Carlos

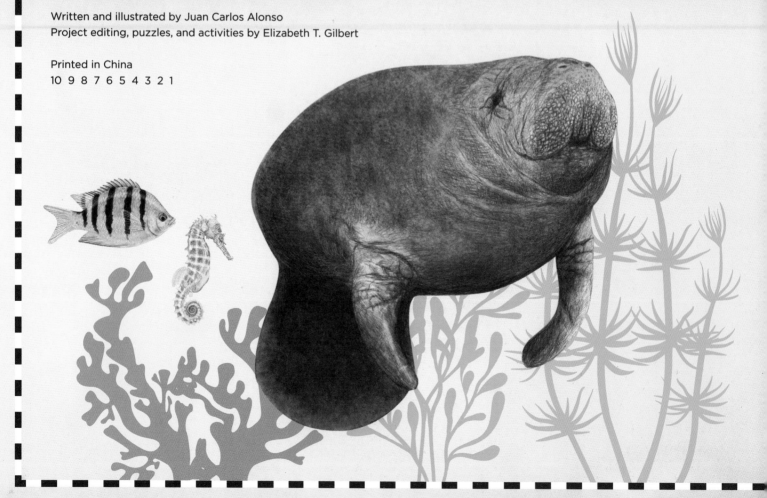

Table of Contents

Introduction

Spanning more than 140,000,000 square miles (362,600,000 km²) and covering more than 70 percent of Earth's surface, the ocean is by far our world's largest habitat. Yet, scientists say that only 5 percent of our oceans have been explored. We still have so much to learn about the planet we live on.

Though a lot still remains to be discovered, there are close to a million animal species already documented on Earth. To better organize and understand the relationships between each species, scientists called taxonomists have categorized animals using the International Code of Zoological Nomenclature, or ICZN. This system divides each animal into seven levels: Kingdom, Phylum, Class, Order, Family, Genus, and finally Species. Some animals are further classified as a subspecies, meaning they are related to the same species, but have developed their own physical traits further differentiating them from the species they belong to.

Common Bottlenose Dolphin

If we take a Common Bottlenose Dolphin, for instance, it would be classified as follows:

Kingdom: Animalia meaning it is an animal

Phylum: Chordata referring to the spinal cord or vertebrate

Class: Mammalia meaning it is a mammal

Order: Cetacea meaning it belongs to the group of marine mammals including whales

Family: Delphinidae meaning it is in the dolphin family

Genus: Tursiops meaning it belongs to oceanic dolphins

Species: truncatus meaning it belongs to a group with specific shared traits

Its scientific name is therefore:

Tursiops truncatus (Note that the species name is never capitalized)

Oceans of the World

Earth has an interconnected body of salt water called the World Ocean. It is divided into five main areas: the Pacific Ocean, the Atlantic Ocean, the Indian Ocean, the Southern Ocean, and the Arctic Ocean. Smaller bodies of salt water—gulfs, seas, and bays—are distinct from the oceans because they are near large land masses. The oceans play a role in controlling temperature and weather across the globe; they transfer heat from warmer areas near the equator to the colder polar regions through currents. This movement of warm and cold water significantly impacts everything from ice melting or freezing to precipitation and larger weather patterns. It's safe to say all life on Earth depends on the health of our oceans.

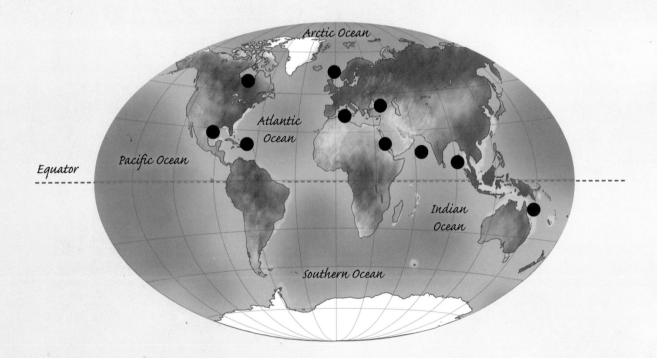

Seas, Bays, and Gulfs of the Oceans	1. Hudson Bay	4. North Sea	7. Red Sea	9. Bay of Bengal
	2. Gulf of Mexico	5. Mediterranean Sea	8. Arabian Sea	10. Coral Sea
	3. Caribbean Sea	6. Black Sea		

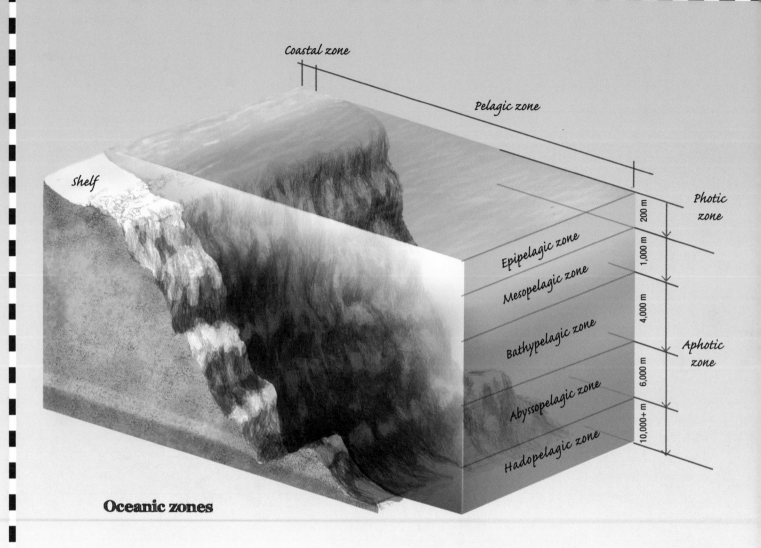

Oceanic zones

The ocean is about 12,000 feet (3,658 meters) deep, on average. The deepest point, the Mariana Trench, is about 6.8 miles (10,971 meters) deep. The oceans are divided into different zones based on their depth, called oceanic zones. From shallowest to deepest, they are: Epipelagic, Mesopelagic, Bathypelagic, Abyssopelagic, and Hadopelagic. See the above image to learn their depth ranges.

Sunlight can only travel through the first 650 feet (192 meters) of salt water. This sunlit layer of the ocean is called the Photic zone. Directly beneath this zone is the Aphotic zone, which contains little or no light. As you travel through the Aphotic zone downward, it becomes increasingly darker.

At depths below 3,281 feet (1,000 meters), there is nothing but absolute darkness. The water also gets colder, dropping to 32 to 39 degrees Fahrenheit (0 to 4 degrees Celsius).

The oceans are also divided into two general horizontal zones: the Coastal and Pelagic zones. The coastal zone is made of shallow water near coastlines. The Pelagic zone is the open ocean away from the coast.

Marine Animals

Marine animals are animals that live in or rely on the ocean for their existence. Most, such as fish or whales, live fulltime in the water. Others, such as polar bears, seals, and penguins, spend equal time in the water and on dry land. All marine animals live in a variety of ecosystems, ranging from mangroves to coral reefs to the deep sea, each with its own distinct and expansive diversity.

There are more than 230,000 known marine animal species, and every year, an average of 2,000 new species are discovered. Oceanographers believe there are more than 2 million species living in the oceans that haven't been discovered yet.

While a lot of marine life is easily visible, so much more of it is small and impossible to see without a microscope. Billions of tiny living organisms, including plants, animals, bacteria, and protozoa, live in ocean water. These organisms are called plankton. There are many types of plankton, from single-celled organisms to eggs and even young stages of larger animals (such as fish and crustaceans). Plankton can be divided into two main groups: zooplankton, which represents a wide variety of organisms classified as animals; and phytoplankton, which represents the organisms classified as plants.

Zooplankton

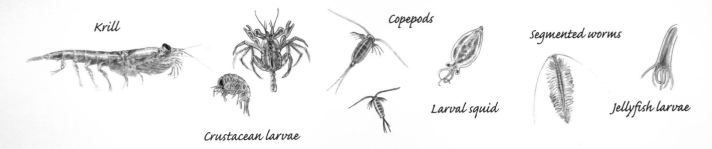

Krill

Copepods

Segmented worms

Crustacean larvae

Larval squid

Jellyfish larvae

Phytoplankton

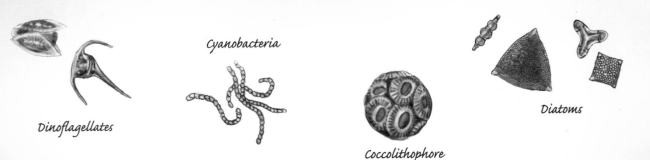

Cyanobacteria

Dinoflagellates

Coccolithophore

Diatoms

Marine Food Webs

A food web is a diagram that illustrates how energy is transferred from organism to organism. It begins with producers, which are organisms that can produce their own food. Like plants on land, marine producers use energy from the sun and photosynthesis to make food. Phytoplankton are the most widespread marine producers. They are the primary basis of the marine food web. Zooplankton eat phytoplankton for energy. Smaller fish and filter feeders eat zooplankton for energy, and bigger fish eat the smaller fish. The energy travels up through levels, from basic organisms to the top predators in the ecosystem. These levels are called trophic levels.

The food web is made up of several food chains within each ecosystem. Each species within an ecosystem is important to the food web and can impact the survival of other species. Marine ecologists pay special attention to habitat, populations, and interactions between organisms, and how changes in our environment can affect their survival.

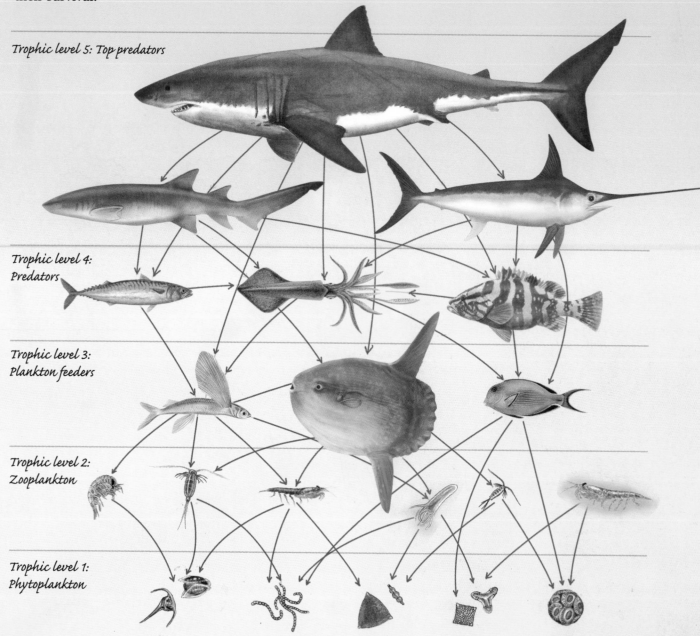

Trophic level 5: Top predators

Trophic level 4: Predators

Trophic level 3: Plankton feeders

Trophic level 2: Zooplankton

Trophic level 1: Phytoplankton

Sizes not to scale.

Marine Plants

In addition to phytoplankton, the ocean is home to several types of plants. Seaweed, kelp, seagrass, and algae grow in shallow, coastal waters where there is just enough light for them to thrive. These plants serve as food to a number of animals—from crustaceans and sea turtles to some types of fish and even humans.

Did You Know?

Coral and sponges may seem like plants because they don't move, but they're actually animals!

Brain Coral Maze

Brain coral is a type of coral with a ridged surface that resembles—you guessed it—a brain! Make your way through the twists and turns of this maze to see if you come out the other side.

ANSWER ON PAGE 156

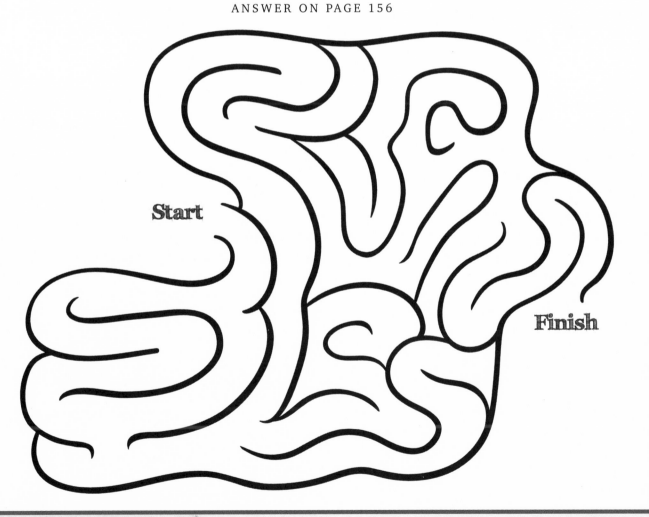

In the following pages we will explore different marine mammals, fish, birds, reptiles, and cephalopods. We will look at each group's unique features and adaptations, as well as their relationships with other animals that rely on each other in a vast community of life on Earth.

Marine Mammals

Like their counterparts on land, marine mammals are warm-blooded and have mammary glands that produce milk to feed their young. There are three primary orders of marine mammals: Carnivora (polar bears, sea otters, and seals), Cetacea (whales), and Sirenia (manatees and dugongs). Most species have specialized adaptations for life in the ocean. These include fur and a thick layer of fat called blubber used as insulation against cold water and as a food reserve. Many marine mammals are able to reduce their heart rate while underwater and reduce blood flow to nonessential organs, which allows them to remain without breathing for long periods of time; this is called bradycardia.

Order: Carnivora, Cetacea, and Sirenia

Species: More than 130

Size Range: 3.7 feet (1.1 meters), Marine Otter, to 100 feet (30 meters), Blue Whale

Weight Range: 13 pounds, Marine Otter, to 300,000 pounds, Blue Whale

Distribution: All oceans worldwide

Habitat: From warm, tropical waters to cold Arctic and Antarctic waters

Facts: All marine mammals, including whales, have hair. Many whale species lose their hair shortly after birth. The largest animal known to have ever lived is the blue whale. The deepest-diving marine mammal, the Cuvier's beaked whale, is capable of diving 1.9 miles (3 kilometers).

Marine Mammal Orders

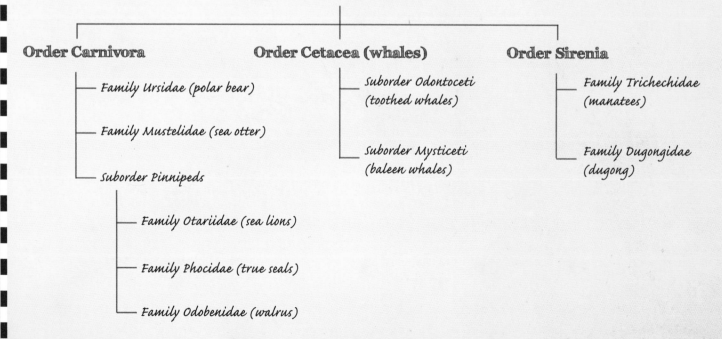

Order Carnivora
- Family Ursidae (polar bear)
- Family Mustelidae (sea otter)
- Suborder Pinnipeds
  - Family Otariidae (sea lions)
  - Family Phocidae (true seals)
  - Family Odobenidae (walrus)

Order Cetacea (whales)
- Suborder Odontoceti (toothed whales)
- Suborder Mysticeti (baleen whales)

Order Sirenia
- Family Trichechidae (manatees)
- Family Dugongidae (dugong)

Humpback Whale

(Megaptera novaeangliae)
Found in all oceans across the world, they generally prefer to stay closer to coastlines for feeding. For more information, see page 53.

Humpback whale babies, called calves, are born measuring up to 15 feet (4.5 meters) in length and weighing more than a ton

Did You Know?

Marine mammals care for their young by providing nourishment and protection. For some species, like humpback whales, this care can last up to a year.

Polar Bear

Polar bears are the only members of the bear family to be classified as marine mammals. They spend their lives on and around the land masses associated with the polar ice caps and across the Arctic Ocean. A thick coat and undercoat of waterproof hair, as well as a layer of fat, protect them from the harsh, cold weather. Polar bears have all-black skin that absorbs and retains heat from the sun; almost entirely covered in fur, their dark skin is only visible on their noses and foot pads. Using their developed sense of smell and vision, polar bears hunt ringed and bearded seals. They are also known to eat beluga whales and scavenge carcasses of dead animals.

Did You Know?

Polar bear paws are enormous, reaching over 1 foot (30 centimeters) wide. Their broad size helps them walk over deep snow and swim through water.

Polar Bear

(Ursus maritimus)
Found throughout the Arctic Circle inhabiting ice caps of frozen water.
Length: 9 to 10 feet (2.9 meters)
Weight: 700 to 1,500 pounds
Conservation status: Vulnerable

Broad, large head

Massive body covered in two layers of dense, oily, and water-repellent fur

Short tail measuring only 4 inches (10 centimeters)

Polar bears generally move at a slow pace to conserve energy, but are capable of quick bursts of speed

Thick, muscular legs

Foot pads are covered in papillae, or bumps, that help to keep them from slipping on ice

Small eyes

Distinctive arch on top of snout

Small, rounded ears

Large, sharp teeth designed to capture moving prey

Word Jumble

Can you guess what the jumbled-up words are in the fact below?

ANSWER ON PAGE 156

The fur of a polar bear is

K I C T H,

O P R A F E R T O W,

and T I W E H.

Sea Otter

The Mustelidae family is a broad family of mammals including weasels, polecats, ferrets, badgers, and wolverines. There are only two species that are classified as marine mammals: the marine otter and the sea otter. The marine otter (*Lontra felina*) spends much of its time out of the water. At 3.7 feet (1.1 meters), they are the smallest of all the marine mammals. Sea otters (*Enhydra lutris*) spend the vast majority of their time in the water, only occasionally going on shore to groom or nurse their young. Sea otters mostly forage for food by diving to the ocean floor. Once they get food, they float on the surface of the water on their backs and eat off their bellies. Sea otters are known to use stones as tools to break open clam shells or crabs to get to the meat.

Did You Know?

Sea otters don't have blubber or large fat deposits to keep warm. Instead, they rely on their thick coat of fur.

Sea otters remain close to shorelines and live in waters 50 to 75 feet (15 to 23 meters) deep where they can dive to forage

Large, webbed, hind feet and semi-flattened tail are used to swim efficiently

Place sticker here

The sea otter has the thickest coat of fur in the animal kingdom at nearly 1 million strands per square inch (2.5 centimeters).

Sea Otter

(Enhydra lutris)

Found along coastlines of the Pacific Ocean from the United States and Canada to Eastern Russia.

Length: 3 to 4 feet (0.9 to 1.2 meters)
Weight: 49 to 100 pounds
Conservation status: Endangered

Nostrils close to prevent water from entering

Small ears close when submerged

Draw a Sea Otter

Use the blank grid to draw what you see in each square of the sea otter portrait. Start with a sketch, and then give it a thick, furry coat with markers, colored pencils, or crayons!

Did You Know?

A sea otter's lungs help it both float and dive for long periods of time.

Mammal Smarts Word Search

Get to know these important words as you learn about mammals of the ocean! If you don't know what a word means, you might find it in the glossary on page 160. Can you spot all the words below?

ANSWERS ON PAGE 156

- ☐ Baleen
- ☐ Blowhole
- ☐ Blubber
- ☐ Bradycardia
- ☐ Calf
- ☐ Echolocation
- ☐ Flippers
- ☐ Fluke
- ☐ Forage
- ☐ Melon

```
Z F L I P P E R S Q M E B S E E Q S L M
A I O O T F B B E H S R G O C N S R G H
K D I R C Y S R S K F I I Z H S Z Y L B
G C A Z A J T A S V M R W F O H C A Q U
K H K D L G M D R Q C H E K L Z T S L F
M Q I K L F E Y G Q W W M B O J B H Y R
Z M N M O E C C Z H V V H T C A D Q C P
Y U F X L U M A C M V W U T A B F P N Z
H W J C O E L R J L L M Y A T O L J W G
M E S H K Z F D Z Q C J L E I C E D B L
G M A A S X N I X M F P X D O I M W L Q
Z E O X J D M A D W E L G E N M W K O Q
F U A P I P X B G Y S S O Z A E Q E W K
B L C I Z I F D D Z Z T J Z A L E S H O
A T U Q W J M V Z V A I R U L O W Z O P
L O K K B L U B B E R K A V B N F M L D
E Z I K E L V E D O P M C A L F X J E D
E Y F U H G G M G C X Z G Y G Q V U T U
N L J D F S D P D T N F J X W W C V I T
S V V S D J W J W L P F C E P X X W B K
```

True Seals

Pinnipedia, meaning "fin-footed," is a suborder of marine mammals of three families: Phocidae, true or earless seals; Otariidae, eared seals (fur seals and sea lions); and Odobenidae, whose only living species is the walrus. Pinnipeds are fully adapted to life in the ocean, but their well-developed sight and smell work equally well on land.

The family Phocidae consists of 19 species of true seals or earless seals. Unlike the family Otariidae, they don't have an external ear; instead, they have a small hole with a functioning inner ear. On land they move awkwardly; they roll on their bellies while using the claws on their front flippers to push forward, giving them the name crawling seals.

Bearded Seal
(*Erignathus barbatus*)
Found across the upper Arctic Circle, bearded seals feed mostly on clams, fish, and squid.
Length: 6 to 8 feet (1.8 to 2.4 meters)
Weight: 440 to 950 pounds
Conservation status: Least Concern

Relatively small head

Large body covered in thick layer of blubber

Thick, coarse whiskers give a "bearded" appearance

True Seal Identity

Can you identify each type of seal?
Match their descriptions by writing the correct letters in the boxes below!
ANSWERS ON PAGE 156

A—Harbor Seal
(Phoca vitulina)
Harbor seals have cylindrical-shaped bodies streamlined for swimming, a spotted coat that ranges in color from blue-gray to brown-tan, noses capable of closing underwater, and long whiskers. Found widespread across the Pacific and Atlantic Oceans in coastal waters ranging from the United States and Canada to northern Europe, harbor seals are separated into five distinct subspecies by geographic areas. They feed on a range of fish, including salmon and anchovies, shrimp, clams, and mollusks.

B—Hooded Seal
(Cystophora cristata)
Hooded seals have thick bodies with black and white markings. Found across the Arctic Ocean and North Atlantic on floating ice packs, hooded seals feed on crustaceans, krill, and fish, including halibut and cod.

C—Ribbon Seal
(Histriophoca fasciata)
Ribbon seals are covered in black skin and fur with distinct white "ribbon" markings. Found across the Arctic portions of the North Pacific Ocean, ribbon seals feed on fish, including pollock and cod, squid, and octopus.

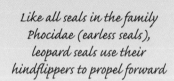

Like all seals in the family Phocidae (earless seals), leopard seals use their hindflippers to propel forward

Long, slender body with spotted pattern

Leopard Seal

(Hydrurga leptonyx)
Found in the cold waters around the Antarctic continent but are known to travel north to southern South America, South Africa, New Zealand, and around the southern coast of Australia. Leopard seals have a diverse diet and are fierce predators, hunting and eating penguins and other seals including Weddell and Antarctic fur seals. They also feed on krill and squid.
Length: 8 to 11.5 feet (2.5 to 3.5 meters)
Weight: 440 to 1,350 pounds
Conservation status: Least Concern

Top Predators

Leopard seals are the second-largest predators in the Antarctic. Can you guess what the largest predator is? Place the sticker of your best guess below!
ANSWER ON PAGE 156

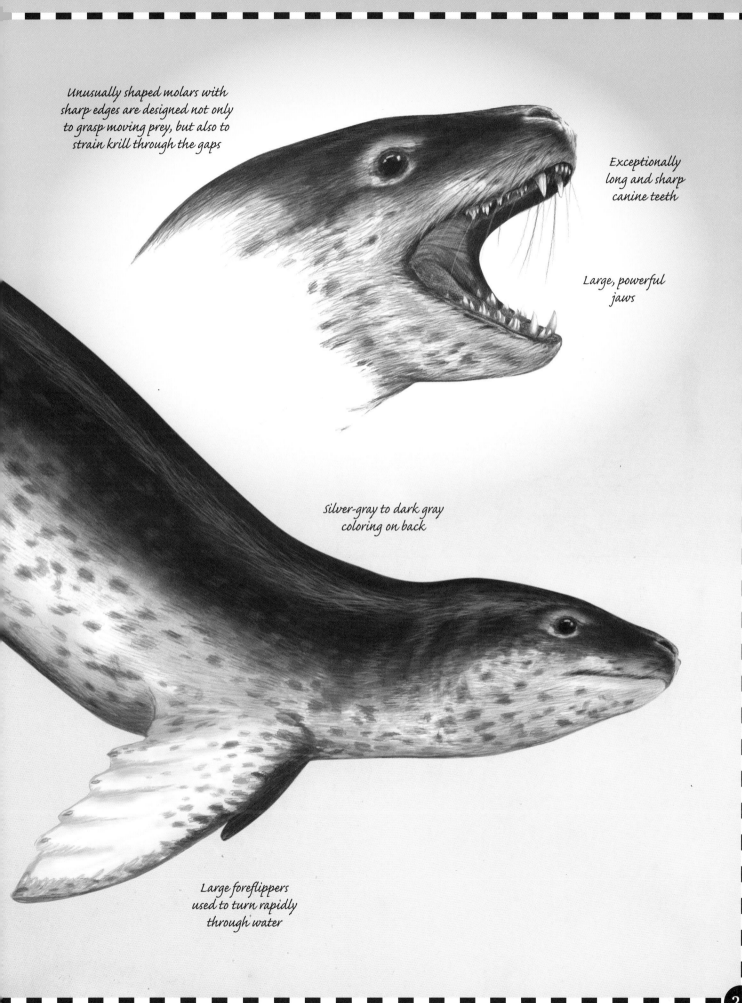

Unusually shaped molars with sharp edges are designed not only to grasp moving prey, but also to strain krill through the gaps

Exceptionally long and sharp canine teeth

Large, powerful jaws

Silver-gray to dark gray coloring on back

Large foreflippers used to turn rapidly through water

Elephant Seals

Elephant seals are comprised of two species: the northern elephant seal (*Mirounga angustirostris*) and the southern elephant seal (*Mirounga leonina*). The southern elephant seal is the largest of all the pinniped species as well as the largest in the Carnivora order (including land species). The males can reach more than 19 feet (5.8 meters) long and weigh as much as 7,000 pounds.

Word Scramble

Unscramble the words below to reveal a fact about elephant seals.

ANSWER ON PAGE 156

HET LTPAHNEE ASEL

SNEO NCA MKEA

EYRV DULO SNDUOS.

Females are much smaller than males and lack a large nose. Males have a mostly hairless, thick neck used to intimidate other males.

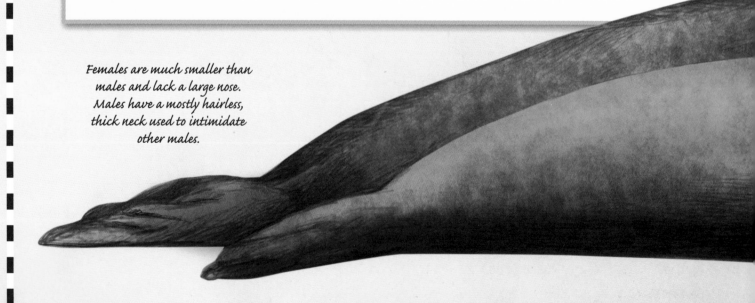

Northern Elephant Seal
(Mirounga angustirostris)

Found across the eastern Pacific coasts across western United States and Canada, northern elephant seals feed mostly on squid, hake (a type of fish), crustaceans, sharks, and rays.

Length: Males are 16 feet (5 meters)
Females are 10 feet (3 meters)
Weight: Males are 3,000 to 5,000 pounds
Females are 800 to 1,900 pounds
Conservation status: Least Concern

Did You Know?

The name "elephant" seal comes from their size and unique nose, not because they are related to elephants.

Eyes are dark with a developed sense for low-light vision to help them capture prey

Large "trunk" lies over its mouth when relaxed

Know the Nose

A "hood" on the head isn't the only unique feature of the hooded seal. When being aggressive, males inflate a balloon-like nasal sac from one of their nostrils.

The harbor seal can close its nose when under water.

Elephant seals expel air through their large noses to make loud sounds that deter other males from their territory.

True or False

Read the three sentences below.
One is true and two are false.
Place a check mark next to the true statement!

ANSWER ON PAGE 156

☐ True seals can smell and see well on land.
☐ True seals can only smell under water.
☐ All true seals have a balloon-like nasal sac.

True Seals Eared Seals

Examples: harbor seals, hooded seals, ribbon seals, leopard seals, and elephant seals

Examples: Steller sea lions and California sea lions

Short Snout

Long whiskers

No external ear

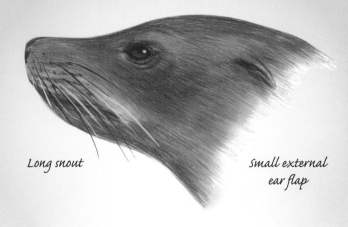

Long snout

Small external ear flap

Prominent claws used to grasp ground for locomotion

Short flippers covered in hair

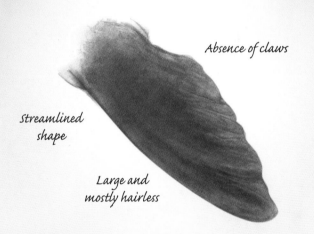

Absence of claws

Streamlined shape

Large and mostly hairless

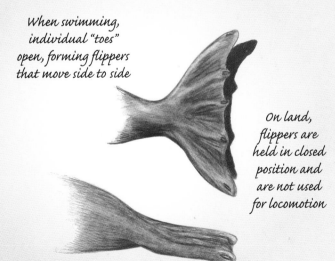

When swimming, individual "toes" open, forming flippers that move side to side

On land, flippers are held in closed position and are not used for locomotion

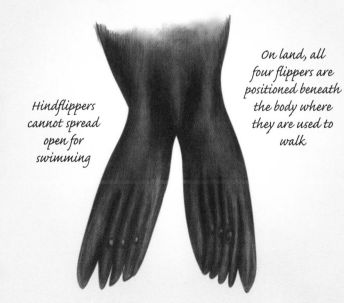

Hindflippers cannot spread open for swimming

On land, all four flippers are positioned beneath the body where they are used to walk

Eared Seals

The Otariidae family of seals includes 14 species of sea lions and fur seals. They can be found in a variety of places, from polar to temperate climates, and even in the equatorial islands of the Galapagos. Otariids, commonly known as eared seals, are very social, at times forming large colonies of several hundred or more individuals. Within each species the males are much larger than the females, sometimes more than twice the weight. This is called sexual dimorphism. Otariids feed on fish, squid, and krill, and they are capable of diving up to 1,300 feet (400 meters) to find food.

Steller Sea Lion
(Eumetopias jubatus)
Found along the North Pacific coastlines from western United States to northern Japan, Steller sea lions are the largest of all seals in the Otariidae family.
Length: Males are 10.7 feet (3.3 meters)
Females are 8 feet (2.4 meters)
Weight: Males are 2,200 pounds
Females are 700 pounds
Conservation status: Near Threatened

Eared seals are very vocal through their barking and grunting sounds

The male Steller sea lion is massive compared to the female. As they mature, they develop a thick neck.

Sea Lion Labyrinth

Very intelligent and highly flexible, the California sea lion is capable of moving freely and fluidly under water. Help this sea lion wind its way through a maze to reach a tasty meal!

ANSWER ON PAGE 156

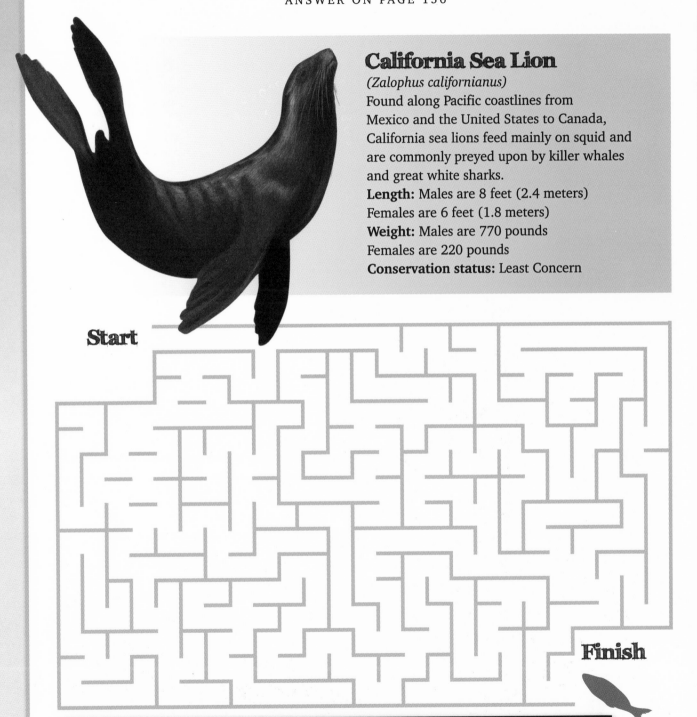

California Sea Lion
(Zalophus californianus)
Found along Pacific coastlines from Mexico and the United States to Canada, California sea lions feed mainly on squid and are commonly preyed upon by killer whales and great white sharks.
Length: Males are 8 feet (2.4 meters)
Females are 6 feet (1.8 meters)
Weight: Males are 770 pounds
Females are 220 pounds
Conservation status: Least Concern

Start

Finish

Did You Know? Otariids walk on all fours, making them more maneuverable on land than true seals.

Walrus

The Odobenidae family is represented by a single species: the walrus (*Odobenus rosmarus*). The species is broken down further into three subspecies, each defined by geographical area: the Atlantic walrus, the Pacific walrus, and the Laptev walrus. All walruses are easily recognizable by the large tusks—more than 3 feet (0.9 meters) in length—protruding from their mouths. Tusks are found on both males and females, though they are usually smaller on females. They share features with both earless and eared seals. Like eared seals, walruses can move on the ground by placing their limbs beneath their bodies; like earless seals, walruses lack the external ear.

By reducing their heart rate when diving, walruses can stay under water for as long as 10 minutes without air

True or False?
Tusks are found only on male walruses.

ANSWER ON PAGE 156

Rear flippers can be positioned under body to move on ground much like a sea lion

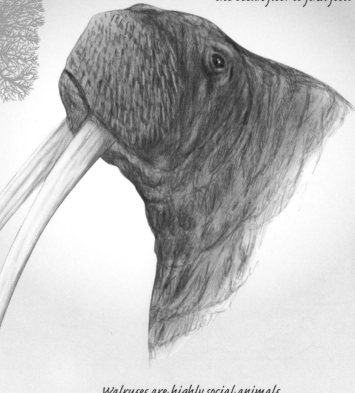

Did You Know?

Walruses have thick skin—more than 3 inches (7.5 centimeters) thick—and a 6-inch (15 centimeters) layer of blubber beneath it!

Coarse whiskers are used as a sensory organ to feel around the ocean floor to find food

Massive canine teeth form large tusks to use for defense, cut through ice, and help get out of the water

Walruses are highly social animals. Males and females spend time in separate groups when not in mating season.

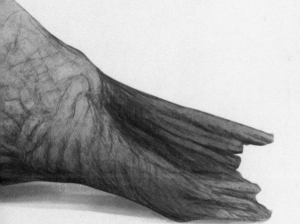

Pacific Walrus

(Odobenus rosmarus divergens)
Found on coastlines around the North Pacific Ocean, from the Bering Strait to northern Russia, Pacific walruses are the largest of the three subspecies. They are opportunistic feeders and will eat a wide variety of food.
Length: 7.5 to 11.5 feet (2.5 to 3.5 meters)
Weight: 1,800 to 3,700 pounds
Conservation status: Vulnerable

Name That Pinniped

Pinnipeds include true seals, eared seals, and walruses. Can you spot the differences in the silhouettes below and name each one correctly?

ANSWERS ON PAGE 156

A: True seal
B: Eared seal
C: Walrus

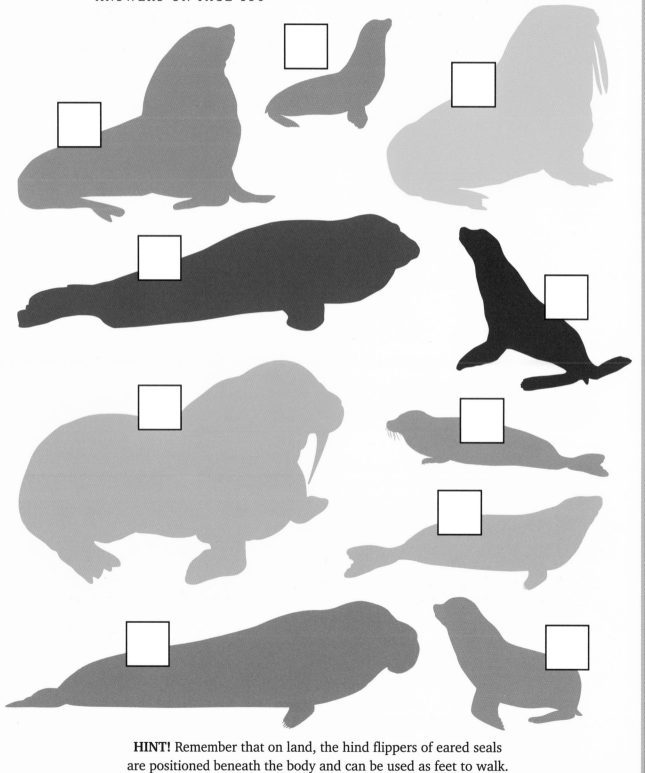

HINT! Remember that on land, the hind flippers of eared seals are positioned beneath the body and can be used as feet to walk.

Test Your Memory

In the previous chapter, you learned about Earth's largest bodies of salt water, including oceans, bays, gulfs, and seas. Can you remember the five oceans? Using the letters on the map as a guide, write the name of each ocean below.

ANSWERS ON PAGE 157

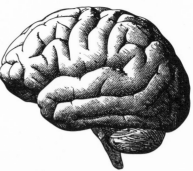

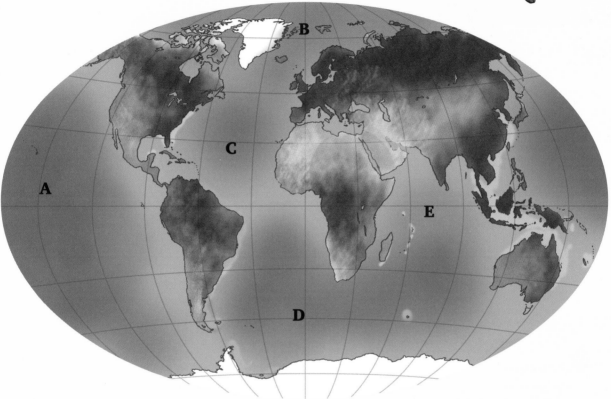

A: _____

B: _____

C: _____

D: _____

E: _____

Did You Know?
The largest and deepest ocean is the Pacific Ocean.

The shallowest ocean is the Arctic Ocean.

The warmest ocean is the Indian Ocean.

The Southern Ocean is sometimes called the "Austral" or "Antarctic Ocean."

Answer Key: Atlantic, Pacific, Indian, Arctic, and Southern

Whales, Dolphins & Porpoises

The cetaceans are comprised of more than 80 species of whales, dolphins, and porpoises in the infraorder Cetacea. They are intelligent and highly specialized for life in the water 100 percent of the time. Cetaceans have smooth, streamlined bodies, nostrils—called blowholes—placed high on their heads, and fins—called flukes—at the end of their bodies used for propulsion. They range greatly in size, from the 3.5-foot-long (1 meter) vaquita porpoise to the 100-foot-long (30 meters) blue whale. Cetaceans are divided into two suborders: Odontoceti for toothed whales (including dolphins and porpoises), and Mysticeti for the baleen whales (including some of the largest whale species). Members of the Odontoceti suborder have developed the sense of echolocation. By emitting and retrieving sound waves from a bulbous organ in their foreheads, they can "see" objects around them, even in deep water where there is no light. Mysticeti species, on the other hand, find food by filling their mouths with water and using rows of hair-like plates in their mouths called baleen as a filter to capture small fish and krill.

Cetacea Order

Odontoceti (toothed whales)

- Family Delphinidae (dolphins)
- Family Phocoenidae (porpoises)
- Family Physeteroidea (sperm whale)
- Family Monodontidae (beluga, narwhal)
- Family Ziphiidae (beaked whales)

Mysticeti (baleen whales)

- Family Balaenopteridae (rorquals: blue whale, sei whale, fin whale)
- Family Balaenidae (bowhead and right whales)
- Family Eschrichtiidae (gray whale)
- Family Cetotheriidae (pygmy right whale)

Blowholes (top view of head)

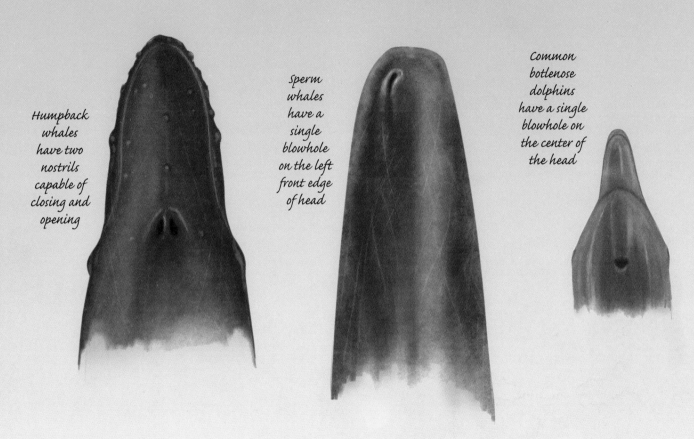

Humpback whales have two nostrils capable of closing and opening

Sperm whales have a single blowhole on the left front edge of head

Common botlenose dolphins have a single blowhole on the center of the head

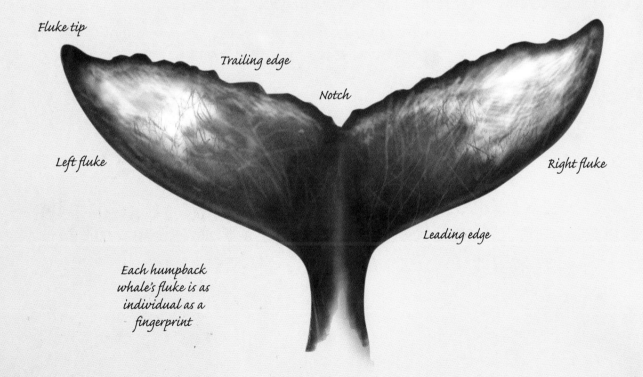

Fluke tip

Trailing edge

Notch

Left fluke

Right fluke

Leading edge

Each humpback whale's fluke is as individual as a fingerprint

Dolphins

Odontoceti is the largest suborder of whales with more than 70 species, all of which are equipped with teeth for catching prey. Odontoceti are divided into five main families: Delphinidae for dolphins; Phocoenidae for porpoises; Monodontidae for the beluga and narwhal; Physeteridae for sperm whales; and Ziphiidae for beaked whales. All species of Odontoceti use echolocation, also called bio sonar, as a means of finding prey.

In total there are 32 members of the Delphinidae family. All members are carnivorous and feed primarily on fish. Some feed on other marine mammals and squid. Delphinids are found in all oceans and seas, and are generally social and live in groups called pods consisting of a few to several thousand individuals, depending on the species.

Place sticker here

Delphinidae is the smartest family of animals in the sea.

Long, broad flukes let the common bottlenose dolphin reach speeds up to 35 miles (56 kilometers) per hour

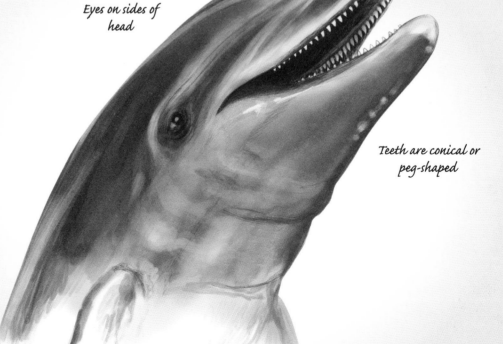

Eyes on sides of head

The melon is a round organ on the top of all toothed whales' heads used to capture images through echolocation

Teeth are conical or peg-shaped

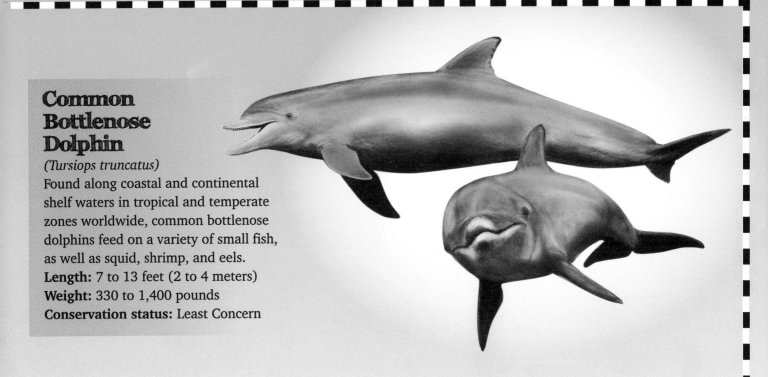

Common Bottlenose Dolphin

(Tursiops truncatus)

Found along coastal and continental shelf waters in tropical and temperate zones worldwide, common bottlenose dolphins feed on a variety of small fish, as well as squid, shrimp, and eels.

Length: 7 to 13 feet (2 to 4 meters)

Weight: 330 to 1,400 pounds

Conservation status: Least Concern

Dolphin Dot-to-Dot

The bottlenose dolphin is one of the most commonly known dolphins in the world. Highly vocal and social, it lives in pods of 2 to 15. It is known for being intelligent, very inquisitive, and playful. Starting at #1, follow the dots to draw your own bottlenose dolphin. Don't forget to add color!

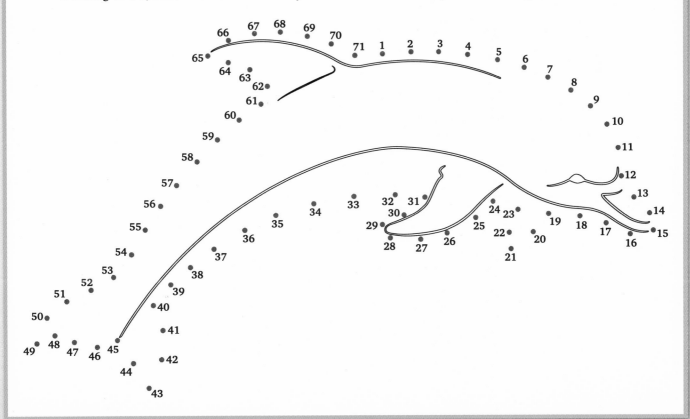

Dolphin Match-up

Can you identify each species of dolphin? Match the images to their descriptions by writing
the correct letters in the boxes on pages 36–38!

ANSWERS ON PAGE 157

☐ Hourglass Dolphin

(*Lagenorhynchus cruciger*)

Description: Large dorsal fin. Short in
length, but tall body. White "hourglass"
markings on sides against black body.
Size: 5.75 feet (1.7 meters), 200 pounds
Diet: Small fish and squid
Location: Waters around the Antarctic
Conservation status: Least Concern

☐ Hector's Dolphin

(*Cephalorhynchus hectori*)

Description: Small, stocky body with a
short beak, rounded dorsal fin, and unique
white markings on the underside.
Size: 4 feet (1.2 meters), 100 pounds
Diet: Fish (herring and mullet) and squid
Location: Coasts of New Zealand
Conservation status: Endangered

☐ Southern Right Whale Dolphin

(*Lissodelphis peronii*)

Description: No dorsal fin and a black top with
a white or cream color underneath.
Size: 9.5 feet (3 meters), 220 pounds
Diet: Small fish and squid
Location: Southern oceans worldwide
Conservation status: Data Deficient

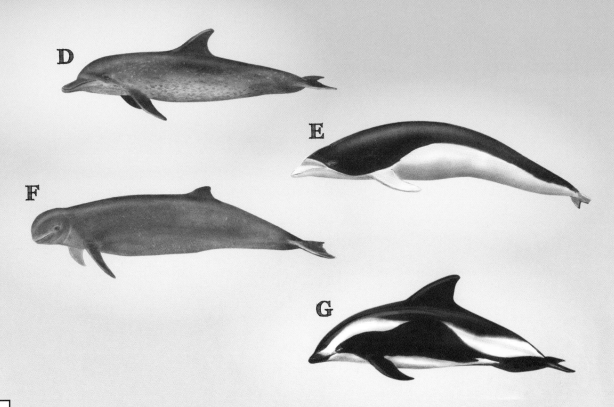

D

E

F

G

☐ **White-Beaked Dolphin**
(*Lagenorhynchus albirostris*)
Description: Tall, rounded dorsal fin and a very short beak.
Size: 10 feet (3 meters), 780 pounds
Diet: Cod, haddock, and other coldwater fish
Location: Sub-Arctic waters of the North Atlantic Ocean
Conservation status: Least Concern

☐ **Atlantic Spotted Dolphin**
(*Stenella frontalis*)
Description: Light and dark spots along body.
Size: 7.5 feet (2.3 meters), 310 pounds
Diet: Squid and small fish
Location: Temperate zones of the Atlantic Ocean
Conservation status: Data Deficient

☐ **Long-Finned Pilot Whale**
(*Globicephala melas*)
Description: Thick, heavy body. Pectoral fins are long and pointed backward.
Size: 22 feet (6.7 meters), 2,900 pounds
Diet: Squid
Location: Temperate and sub-polar zones of the North Atlantic
Conservation status: Data Deficient

☐ **Irrawaddy Dolphin**
(*Orcaella brevirostris*)
Description: Rounded, well-defined head with a minimal beak and a small dorsal fin set toward the tail.
Size: 7.5 feet (2.3 meters), 440 pounds
Diet: Small fish, cephalopods, and crustaceans
Location: Tropical waters of the Indo-Pacific Ocean
Conservation status: Vulnerable

☐ **Short-Beaked Common Dolphin**
(*Delphinus delphis*)
Description: Golden color on the sides of the body.
Size: 9 feet (2.7 meters), 440 pounds
Diet: Small fish, squid, and octopus
Location: Tropical waters of the Atlantic, Pacific, and southeast Indian Oceans
Conservation status: Least Concern

☐ **Indo-Pacific Humpbacked Dolphin**
(*Sousa chinensis*)
Description: Adults have a pink color. Long, pronounced beak and a hump around the dorsal fin.
Size: 9 feet (3 meters), 440 pounds
Diet: Fish and squid
Location: Coasts of the Indian and western Pacific Oceans
Conservation status: Near Threatened

☐ **Risso's Dolphin**
(*Grampus griseus*)
Description: Rounded head with a tall dorsal fin.
Size: 10 feet (3 meters), 1,100 pounds
Diet: Squid and octopus
Location: Temperate and tropical waters worldwide
Conservation status: Least Concern

ANSWERS ON PAGE 157

Sea-doku

Solve these sudoku puzzles using the symbols below. Remember: A symbol can only appear once in each column, row, and box (2 x 2 squares). Good luck!

ANSWERS ON PAGE 157

Killer Whale

Killer whales, also called orcas, are the undisputed apex predator in all oceans. Even though they are commonly called whales, they are actually a part of the dolphin family. They are even known to hunt and eat great white sharks.

Killer Whale
(Orcinus orca)

Found in all oceans worldwide (although they prefer colder far northern and southern waters), killer whales are the largest of all Delphinidae or dolphin species. Killer whales feed on a variety of prey, including fish such as salmon and sharks, as well as sea turtles, seals, and large baleen whales.

Length: Males are 30 feet (9 meters)
Females are 26 feet (8 meters)
Weight: Males are 12,000 pounds
Females are 6,000 pounds
Conservation status: Data Deficient

Tall, upright dorsal fin reaching more than 6 feet tall (1.8 meters)

48 to 52 4-inch-long (10 centimeters) teeth for capturing prey and cutting meat

Large, rounded pectoral fins

White eye spot behind eyes

Gray "saddle" markings behind dorsal fin are less prominent on females

Males are substantially larger than females and can weigh twice as much

Underside of tail is white with a black edge

Killer Whales of Antarctica

Though the killer whale is one species with no subspecies, there are three recognized body types in oceans surrounding Antarctica:

Type A: typical of the species, lives in open oceans, and hunts mostly minke whales

Type B: smaller than type A and lives close to ice packs where it feeds on seals

Type C: smallest of all three types and spends its time under ice packs feeding on fish

Killer Whales of the Arctic

In northern waters surrounding the Arctic Circle, there are three recognized types of orcas:

Resident orca: lives in large pods or groups and feeds mostly on fish

Transient orca: lives in smaller pods and hunts seals, dolphins, and large whales

Offshore orca: lives in open oceans in smaller pods of a dozen or fewer and feeds on schooling fish

Porpoises

The Phocoenidae family of marine mammals includes six species of porpoises. Porpoises are generally smaller than dolphins and have short jaws with no beaks. Their teeth are flattened and spade-shaped, whereas dolphin teeth are typically conical or peg-like. Porpoises live around or near coastlines and usually stay away from the open ocean. Some species favor polar regions. Like all dolphins, they use bio sonar or echolocation to hunt.

Porpoise Match-up

Can you identify each species of porpoise?
Match the images to their descriptions by writing the correct letters in the boxes below!
ANSWERS ON PAGE 157

☐ Vaquita Porpoise
(Neophocaena phocaenoides)
Description: Short, rounded body with a tall dorsal fin for its small size.
Size: 3.5 feet (1 meter), 95 pounds
Diet: Crustaceans, small fish, octopus, and squid
Location: Gulf of California
Conservation status: Critically Endangered

☐ Burmeister's Porpoise
(Phocoena spinipinnis)
Description: Long, streamlined body with a small head. Dorsal fin is angled toward the tail.
Size: 6.5 feet (1.9 meters), 190 pounds
Diet: Fish, shrimp, and squid
Location: Coastal Pacific and Atlantic Oceans
Conservation status: Data Deficient

D

E

F

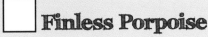 **Finless Porpoise**
(Neophocaena phocaenoides)
Description: Rounded head with a flat nose.
Large pectoral fins but no dorsal fin.
Size: 7.5 feet (2.3 meters), 160 pounds
Diet: Shrimp, squid, crustaceans, and fish
Location: Coastal waters of northern Indian
and western Pacific Oceans
Conservation status: Vulnerable

Spectacled Porpoise
(Phocoena dioptrica)
Description: Dark top with a white underside.
Large, rounded dorsal fin and distinct "speckled"
markings around eyes.
Size: 7.5 feet (2.3 meters), 250 pounds
Diet: Squid, crustaceans, and fish
Location: Sub-Antarctic and low Antarctic waters
Conservation status: Data Deficient

Dall's Porpoise
(Phocoenoides dalli)
Description: White markings on the
underside, dorsal fin, and edges of flukes.
Large hump on back between a triangular
dorsal fin and flukes.
Size: 7.5 feet (2.3 meters), 490 pounds
Diet: Schooling fish and squid
Location: North Pacific Ocean in cold waters
Conservation status: Least Concern

Harbour Porpoise
(Phocoena phocoena)
Description: Wide body with small pectoral
fins and a tall, curved dorsal fin.
Size: 6 feet (1.8 meters), 170 pounds
Diet: Fish, squid, and octopus
Location: Coastal waters of the North Atlantic
and North Pacific Oceans
Conservation status: Least Concern

Sperm Whales

The Physeteroidea family of toothed whales is made up of three species: the sperm whale (*Physeter macrocephalus*), the pygmy sperm whale (*Kogia breviceps*), and the dwarf sperm whale (*Kogia sima*). They range in size from 9 feet (2.7 meters) to more than 60 feet (18 meters) in length. All three species have large, pronounced echolocation organs or melons on their heads, with the sperm whale having the largest in comparable size.

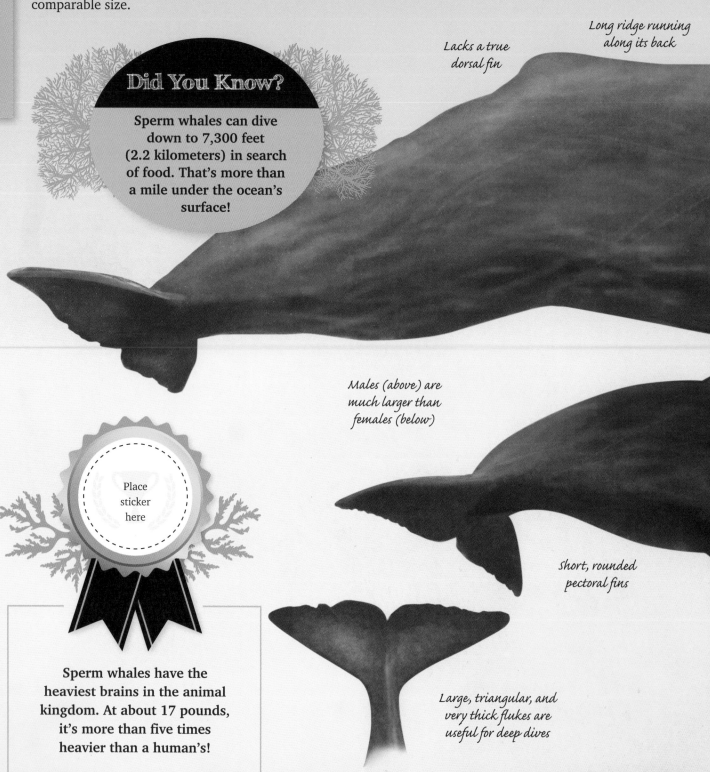

Did You Know?

Sperm whales can dive down to 7,300 feet (2.2 kilometers) in search of food. That's more than a mile under the ocean's surface!

Lacks a true dorsal fin

Long ridge running along its back

Males (above) are much larger than females (below)

Short, rounded pectoral fins

Large, triangular, and very thick flukes are useful for deep dives

Place sticker here

Sperm whales have the heaviest brains in the animal kingdom. At about 17 pounds, it's more than five times heavier than a human's!

Sperm Whale

(Physeter macrocephalus)

Found throughout all oceans (except the Arctic), sperm whales (also known as cachalot) feed primarily on medium-sized squid, giant squid, and fish, including sharks and rays.

Length: Males are 60 feet (18 meters)
Females are 45 feet (14 meters)
Weight: 120,000 pounds
Conservation status: Vulnerable

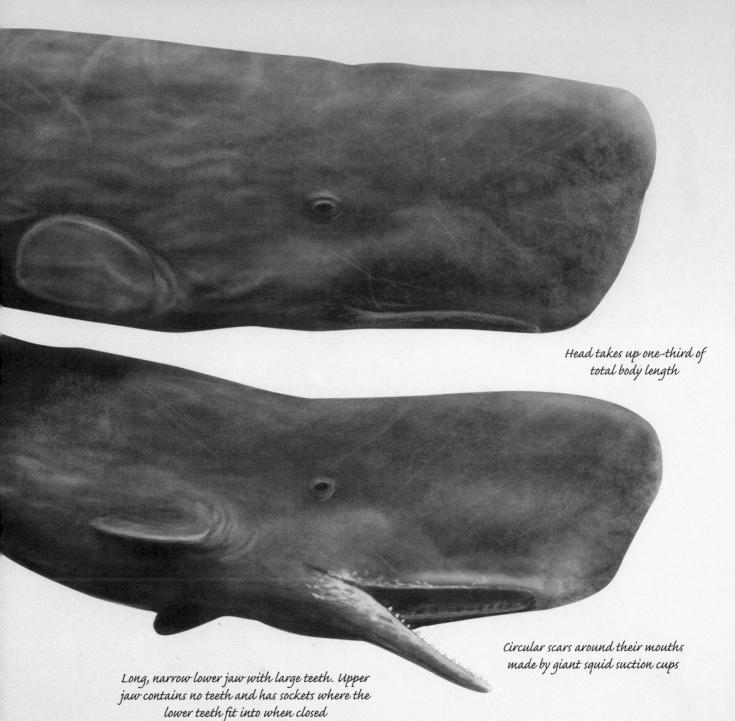

Head takes up one-third of total body length

Circular scars around their mouths made by giant squid suction cups

Long, narrow lower jaw with large teeth. Upper jaw contains no teeth and has sockets where the lower teeth fit into when closed

Echolocation Maze

Compared to its body size, the sperm whale has the largest melon on its head of any animal.
Help this sperm whale use its echolocation skills to make its way through the maze!

ANSWER ON PAGE 157

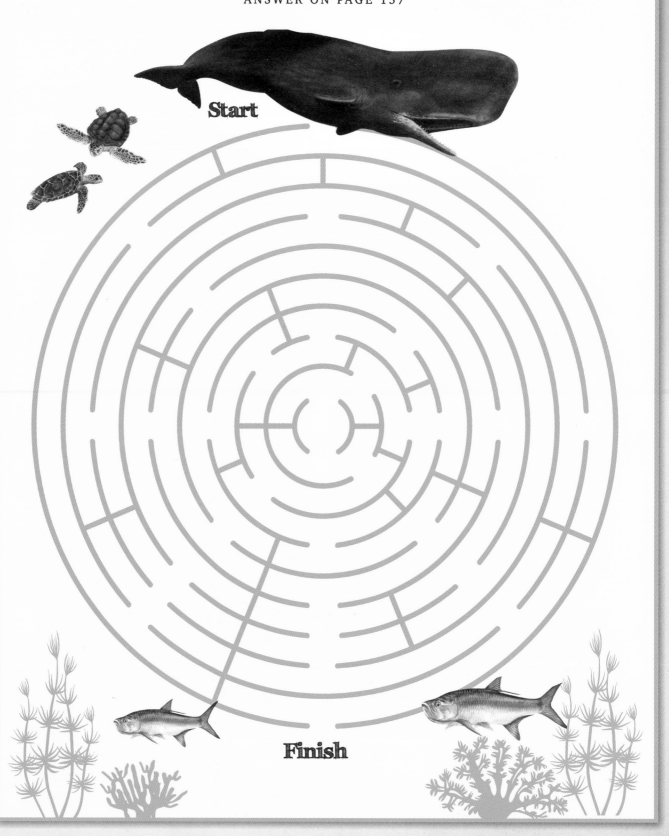

Start

Finish

Sperm Whale Word Scramble

Unscramble the words to reveal facts about the sperm whale!

ANSWERS ON PAGE 157

These master divers can hold their breath under water for about _ _ _ _ _ _ _ _ _ _ _ _ _ at a time.
Sperm whales are big eaters that consume about _ _ _ _ _ _ _ _ _ _ _ pounds of squid and fish per day.
Sperm whales are also called _ _ _ _ _ _ _ _.

_ _ _ _ _ _ _ _ _ _ _ _ _
TINNYE NIMSETU

_ _ _ _ _ _ _ _ _ _ _
WOT DANHOUTS

_ _ _ _ _ _ _ _
ACOCHALT

Beaked Whales

The Ziphiidae family of toothed whales includes 21 species of medium-sized whales ranging in size from the pygmy beaked whale at 13 feet (4 meters) to the Baird's beaked whale at 40 feet (12.8 meters). Also included is the deepest diving mammal, the Cuvier's beaked whale, which is capable of diving 1.9 miles (3 kilometers) deep and holding its breath for more than two hours. Beaked whales are elusive and rarely seen in the wild. They are the least known group of mammals because of their open ocean habitat and small populations.

Long, sloping back with small dorsal fin

Large, broad flukes

Baird's Beaked Whale
(Berardius bairdii)
Found in the cold waters of the North Pacific Ocean, Baird's beaked whales feed on squid, octopus, mackerel, and sardines.
Length: 40 feet (12 meters)
Weight: 31,000 pounds
Conservation status: Data Deficient

Northern Bottlenose Whale
(Hyperoodon ampullatus)
Found in cold water across the North Atlantic Ocean, northern bottlenose whales feed on squid, fish, sea cucumbers, and sea stars.
Length: 37 feet (11.3 meters)
Weight: 17,000 pounds
Conservation status: Data Deficient

Blainville's Beaked Whale
(Mesoplodon densirostris)
Found in tropical and warm waters across all oceans. Blainville's beaked whales feed mostly on squid and live in pods of three to seven individuals.
Length: 15.5 feet (4.7 meters)
Weight: 1,800 pounds
Conservation status: Data Deficient

Flat melon

Arched lower jaw reaches over beak

Small head with pronounced melon

Tusk-like teeth on males

Long, narrow beak

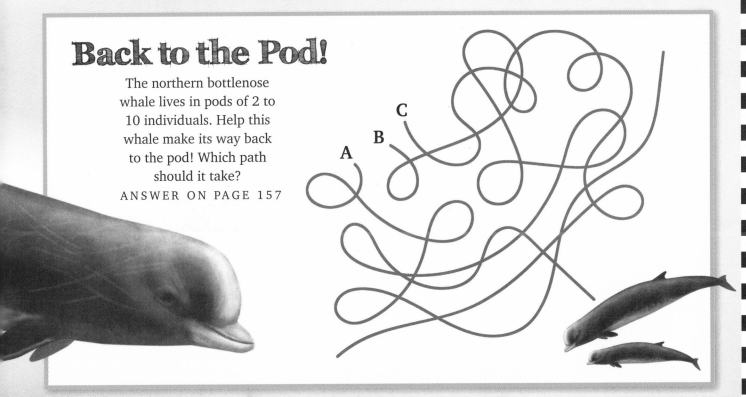

Back to the Pod!

The northern bottlenose whale lives in pods of 2 to 10 individuals. Help this whale make its way back to the pod! Which path should it take?

ANSWER ON PAGE 157

A   B   C

Belugas & Narwhals

The Monodontidae family consists of two unique species: the beluga (*Delphinapterus leucas*) and the narwhal (*Monodon monoceros*). Narwhals are notably the most distinctive of all whales due to the enormous tusk protruding from their heads. The beluga is unique due to its all-white coloring. Both are found near and around the Arctic, where they primarily feed on fish and squid.

Place sticker here

Narwhal

(*Monodon monoceros*)
Found across the North Atlantic and Arctic Oceans, narwhals feed on halibut, cod, and flatfish. They live in pods of five to ten individuals.
Length: 18 feet (5.5 meters), head and body (without tusk)
Weight: 3,000 pounds
Conservation status: Near Threatened

The narwhal has the longest tusk of any animal in the sea! The tusk is actually a single canine tooth that grows through the front of the head. Only about 15 percent of female narwhals grow tusks, and about one in 500 males grow two tusks.

Fluke tips point forward

Pectoral fins have curled tips

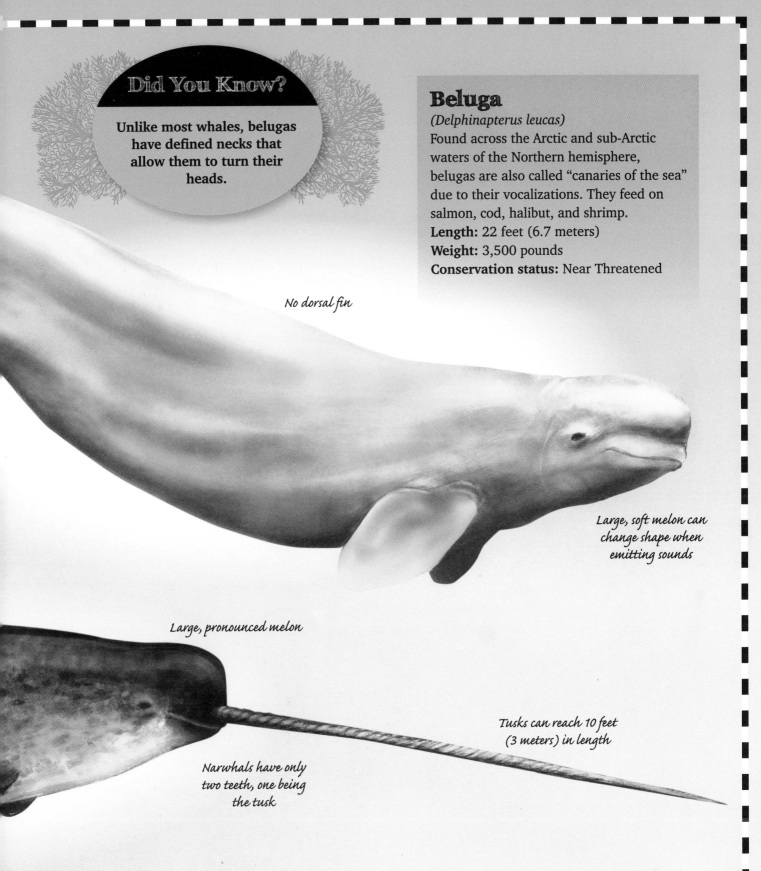

Did You Know?

Unlike most whales, belugas have defined necks that allow them to turn their heads.

Beluga

(Delphinapterus leucas)

Found across the Arctic and sub-Arctic waters of the Northern hemisphere, belugas are also called "canaries of the sea" due to their vocalizations. They feed on salmon, cod, halibut, and shrimp.

Length: 22 feet (6.7 meters)
Weight: 3,500 pounds
Conservation status: Near Threatened

No dorsal fin

Large, soft melon can change shape when emitting sounds

Large, pronounced melon

Tusks can reach 10 feet (3 meters) in length

Narwhals have only two teeth, one being the tusk

Baleen Whales

Mysticeti is an order of cetaceans better known as baleen whales. In contrast to toothed whales, Mysticeti do not have teeth. Instead they have baleen plates on the upper jaws of their mouths. These plates are made of keratin (the same material fingernails are made of) and can grow up to 11.5 feet (3.5 meters) long, depending on the species. Baleen are arranged closely together to form a tight "comb" and act as a filter to strain either krill or small fish from the water it takes into its mouth. Mysticeti is comprised of four families: Balaenopteridae, or rorqual whales; Eschrichtiidae, including the gray whale; Balaenidae, including the right and bowhead whales; and Cetotheriidae, including its only surviving member, the pygmy right whale.

Knobs called tubercles with hair follicles line the mouth area

Wide, thick body tapering at ends

Pectoral fins reaching more than 15 feet (4.5 meters) in length

Baleen Whale Feeding Technique

Baleen plates

1. With its mouth closed, it approaches swarms of krill or schools of fish.

2. It begins to fill its mouth with water and prey.

3. The whale gulps about 15,000 gallons (57,000 liters) of water along with its prey.

4. It expels the water from its mouth and uses its baleen plates as a filter to strain the prey from the water. Then it swallows its food.

Rorqual Whales

The Balaenopteridae family of cetaceans, commonly called rorqual whales, are the largest of the cetaceans and include what is believed to be the largest animal to have ever existed: the blue whale. Rorquals can be identified by long folds of skin called ventral grooves that run on the underside of the mouth and body. These folds are used to expand the mouth, allowing the whale to take in great mouthfuls of water.

Did You Know?

Humpback whales are known for their complex vocalizations that range from howls to cries to moans.

Arch or "hump" around dorsal fin

Flukes reaching more than 15 feet (4.5 meters) from tip to tip

Humpback Whale

(*Megaptera novaeangliae*)
Found in all major oceans from the equator to sub-polar waters, humpback whales feed on krill, plankton, and a variety of small fish.
Length: 55 feet (16.7 meters)
Weight: 80,000 pounds
Conservation status: Least Concern

Crack the Code

Answer the first two questions below based on what you've learned so far.
Use the corresponding symbols to solve the third question!

ANSWERS ON PAGE 157

Which whale has a defined, flexible neck?

The killer whale's coloring is primarily black and .

What is the loudest animal in the ocean (and on Earth)?

Blue Whale

(Balaenoptera musculus)
Found in all oceans worldwide (with the exception of the Arctic),
blue whales feed almost exclusively on krill, taking in an average
of 4 tons daily.
Length: 100 feet (30 meters)
Weight: 300,000 pounds
Conservation status: Endangered

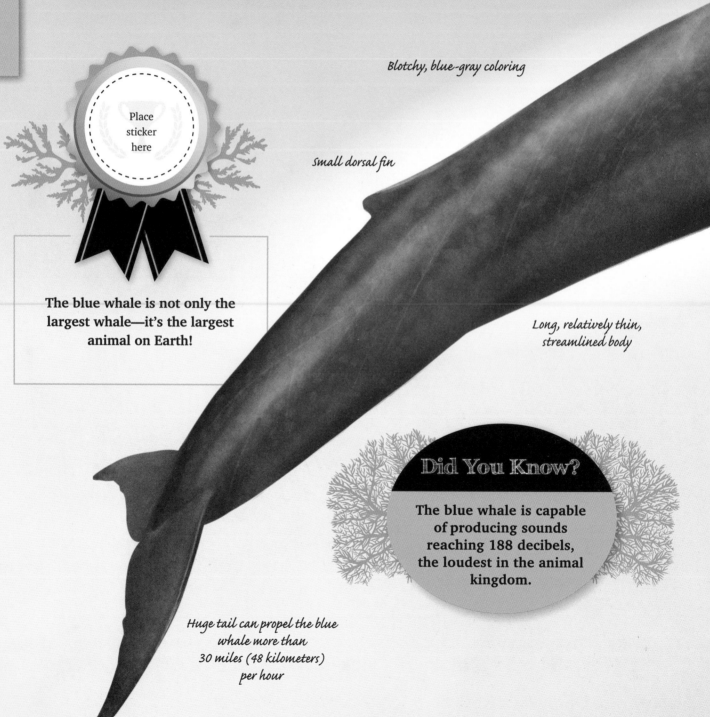

Place sticker here

Blotchy, blue-gray coloring

Small dorsal fin

Long, relatively thin, streamlined body

The blue whale is not only the largest whale—it's the largest animal on Earth!

Did You Know?

The blue whale is capable of producing sounds reaching 188 decibels, the loudest in the animal kingdom.

Huge tail can propel the blue whale more than 30 miles (48 kilometers) per hour

Blowhole

Between 70 to 120 ventral grooves line the underside of throat to midsection

The tail fluke of a blue whale spans 23 to 25 feet (7 to 7.6 meters)

Pectoral fins reaching more than 13 feet (4 meters) in length

Streamlined and triangular-shaped fins

Guess the Size

The blue whale's tongue alone weighs more than which animal? Mark your best guess!

ANSWER ON PAGE 157

Hippopotamus

☐

Elephant

☐

Gorilla

☐

Fin Whale

(Balaenoptera physalus)

Found across all oceans worldwide (with the exceptions of the Arctic and Antarctic extremities), fin whales, also known as finback or common rorqual whales, are the second-largest animals on Earth after the blue whale. They feed on small schools of fish and krill.

Length: 85 feet (26 meters)

Weight: 165,000 pounds

Conservation status: Endangered

Long dorsal fin angled toward tail

The fin whale's powerful tail and large flukes let it reach speeds of more than 23 miles (37 kilometers) per hour

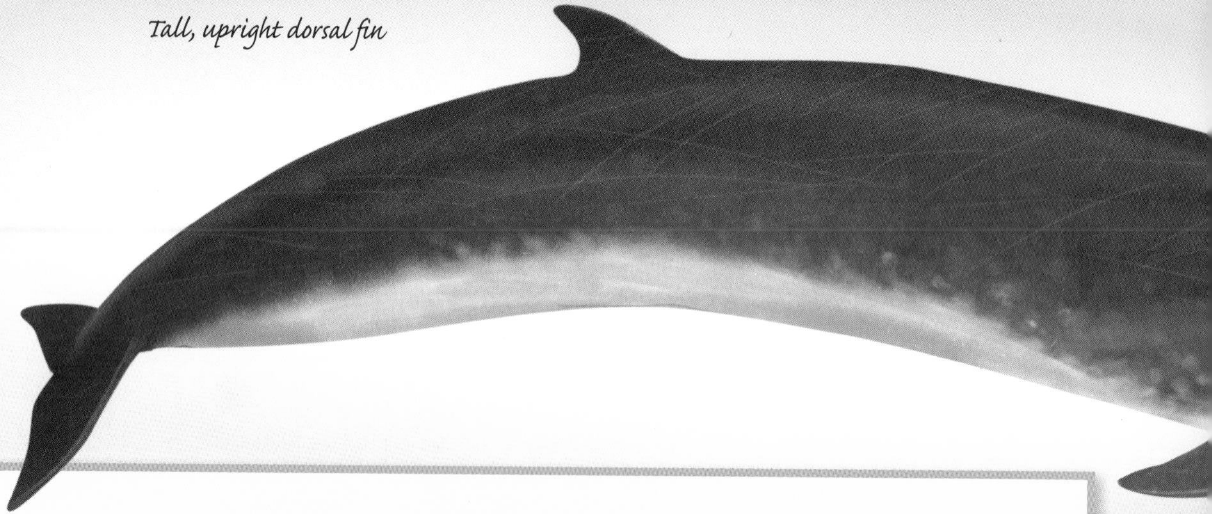

Tall, upright dorsal fin

Take Three!

Take three minutes and see how many words you can make with just the letters from

MARINE MAMMALS

Write your words below.

ANSWERS ON PAGE 157

Relatively small head with blowhole located in front of eyes

small pectoral fins

Sei Whale
(Balaenoptera borealis)
Found across all oceans worldwide (but rarely in polar or tropical waters), sei whales feed on zooplankton, small schooling fish, and krill.
Length: 65 feet (20 meters)
Weight: 62,700 pounds
Conservation status: Endangered

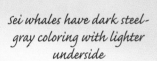

Sei whales have dark steel-gray coloring with lighter underside

30 to 60 ventral grooves spanning from lower jaw to just after pectoral fins

Common Minke Whale
(Balaenoptera acutorostrata)
Found across the cold waters of the North Atlantic and North Pacific Oceans, the common minke whale (also called the northern minke whale) is the smallest of all the rorqual whales. It's also the smaller of two species of minke whales (the other being the Antarctic minke whale). They feed primarily on small schooling fish.
Length: 33 feet (10 meters)
Weight: 20,000 pounds
Conservation status: Data Deficient

White band along center of pectoral fin

Common minke whales have a narrow and pointed head

Gray Whale

The Eschrichtiidae family is represented by a single surviving species: the gray whale. Unlike the rorqual whales, the gray whale has only three to five ventral grooves and feeds by swimming on its side along the ocean floor, gulping and expelling water and mud or sand to capture small invertebrates in its baleen plates.

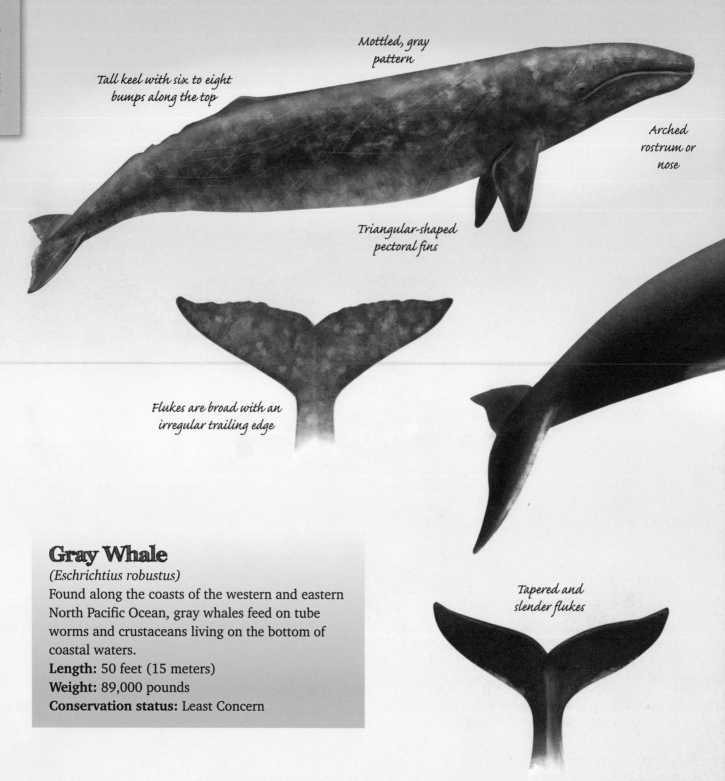

Mottled, gray pattern

Tall keel with six to eight bumps along the top

Arched rostrum or nose

Triangular-shaped pectoral fins

Flukes are broad with an irregular trailing edge

Tapered and slender flukes

Gray Whale
(*Eschrichtius robustus*)
Found along the coasts of the western and eastern North Pacific Ocean, gray whales feed on tube worms and crustaceans living on the bottom of coastal waters.
Length: 50 feet (15 meters)
Weight: 89,000 pounds
Conservation status: Least Concern

Bowhead & Right Whales

The Balaenidae family is comprised of two types of whales: the right whales and the bowhead whale. The right whales include three species divided by geographical area: the North Atlantic, the North Pacific, and the southern right whale. The bowhead whale has only one species: *Balaena mysticetus*. All whales in the Balaenidae family share a unique curved lower jaw that, when closed, conceals enormous baleen plates.

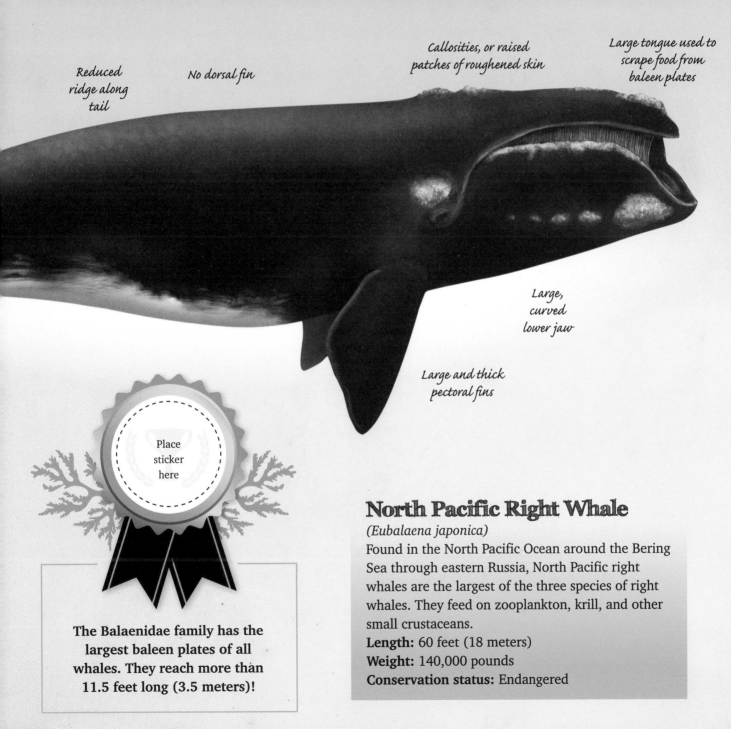

Reduced ridge along tail

No dorsal fin

Callosities, or raised patches of roughened skin

Large tongue used to scrape food from baleen plates

Large, curved lower jaw

Large and thick pectoral fins

Place sticker here

The Balaenidae family has the largest baleen plates of all whales. They reach more than 11.5 feet long (3.5 meters)!

North Pacific Right Whale

(Eubalaena japonica)
Found in the North Pacific Ocean around the Bering Sea through eastern Russia, North Pacific right whales are the largest of the three species of right whales. They feed on zooplankton, krill, and other small crustaceans.

Length: 60 feet (18 meters)
Weight: 140,000 pounds
Conservation status: Endangered

Manatees & Dugongs

The Sirenia order is comprised of two families: Dugongidae, including a single species of dugong; and Trichechidae, including four species of manatees. Both families are fully aquatic and herbivorous, feeding almost exclusively on several species of seagrass. Sirenia inhabit both salt and fresh water, moving from coastal waters of the ocean to inland rivers, lakes, and swamps. Their mouths are angled downward for bottom feeding, with flexible lips that can grab, pull, and uproot grasses.

African Manatee

(Trichechus senegalensis)

Found in coastal and inland waters around the central western coast of Africa, the African manatee feeds primarily on seagrass, but at times feeds on clams, mollusks, and fish found in fishing nets.

Length: 13 feet (4 meters)
Weight: 1,100 pounds
Conservation status: Vulnerable

small eyes

Thick, cylindrical-shaped body

U-shaped mouth angled downward

Dugong

(Trichechus Dugong dugon)

Found in warm coastal and inland waters from the western Pacific Ocean to the eastern coast of Africa, dugongs feed primarily on seagrass, but will occasionally eat jellyfish and shellfish.

Length: 10 feet (3 meters)
Weight: 800 pounds
Conservation status: Vulnerable

Well-defined tail with two lobes, similar to a dolphin's fluke

Where in the World?

Write the name of the correct animal in the map key: **African manatee West Indian manatee, or Dugong.**

○ _____

○ _____

○ _____

ANSWERS ON PAGE 157

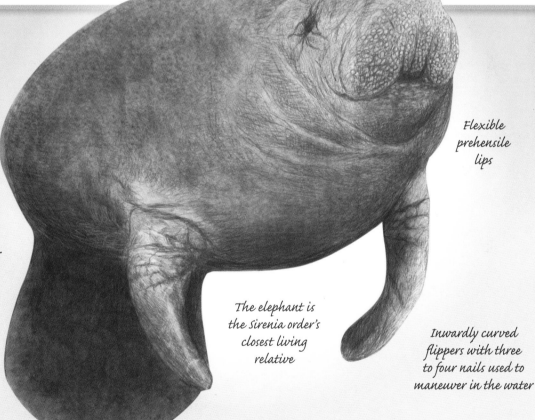

Manatees' and dugongs' bodies are sparsely covered in thick hair called vibrissae (called whiskers on land mammals) that sense touch

Flexible prehensile lips

Large, paddle-like tail used for propulsion

The elephant is the Sirenia order's closest living relative

Inwardly curved flippers with three to four nails used to maneuver in the water

West Indian Manatee

(*Trichechus manatus*)

Found in coastal and inland waters around the lower east coast of the United States and Mexico, the Caribbean, and northern South America, the West Indian manatee feeds on 60 species of aquatic plants in both salt and fresh water. It is also the largest of the Sirenia order.

Length: 14 feet (4.3 meters)

Weight: 1,500 pounds

Conservation status: Vulnerable

What's for Dinner?

Toothed whales, baleen whales, and manatees are all mammals that live their entire lives in water, but they have very different diets! Draw a line from each animal to its appropriate dinner plate.

ANSWERS ON PAGE 158

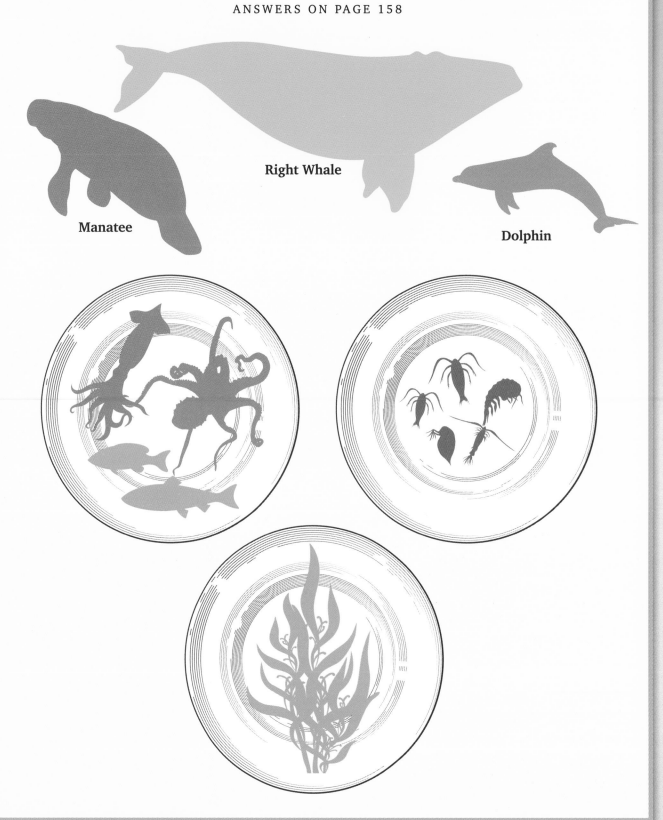

Right Whale

Manatee

Dolphin

Fluke Match-up

Match the fluke to the mammal.

ANSWERS ON PAGE 158

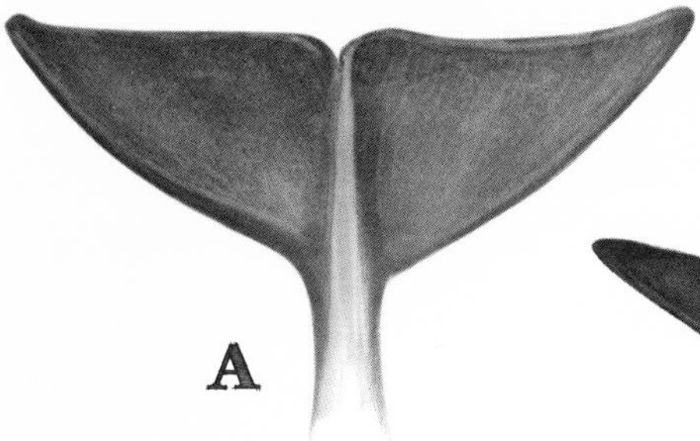

A

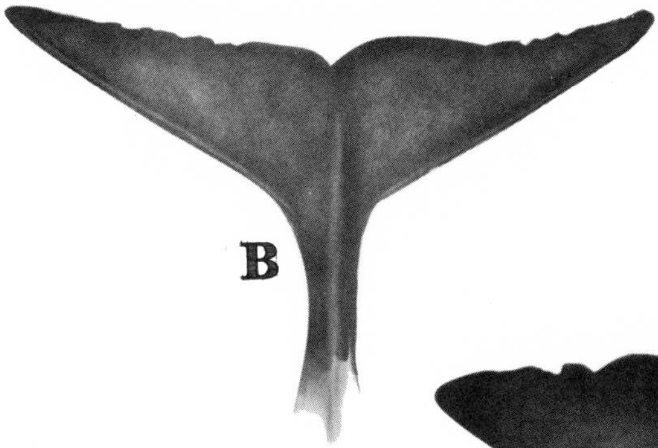

B

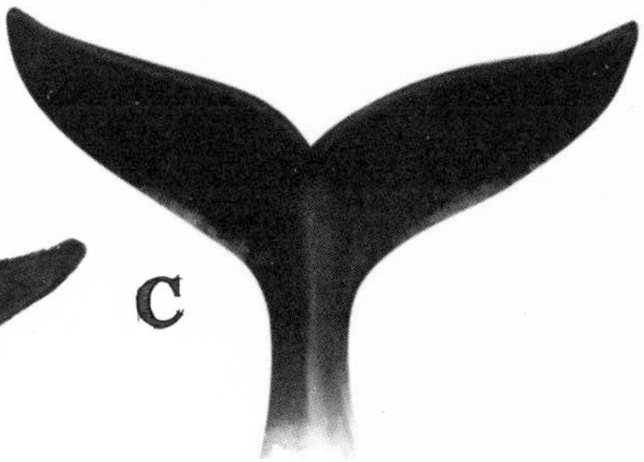

C

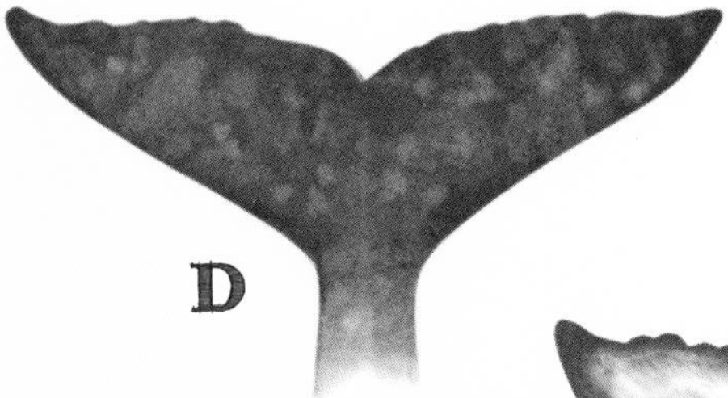

D

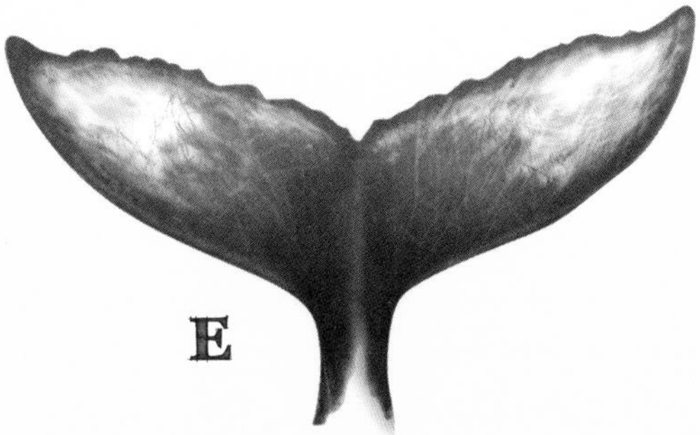

E

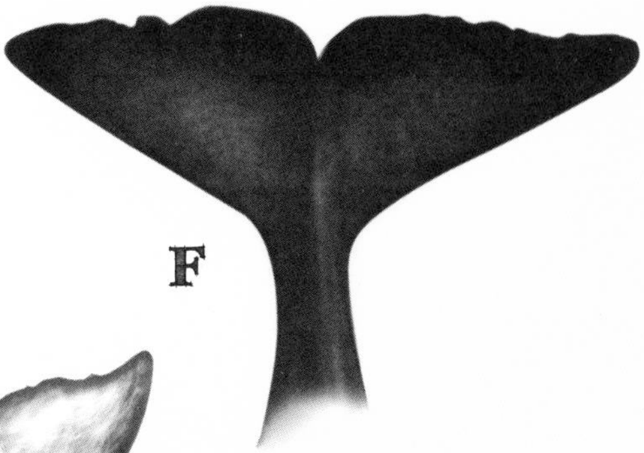

F

☐ **Humpback Whale**

☐ **Blue Whale**

☐ **Gray Whale**

☐ **Sperm Whale**

☐ **Right Whale**

☐ **Bottlenose Dolphin**

HINT! Flip back through this chapter and take a close look at each fluke detail shown.

Marine Fish

Fish are one of the most successful groups of animals on Earth. They have been around for more than 450 million years—outdating the dinosaurs by about 200 million years. There are as many fish species on Earth as there are species of mammals, birds, reptiles, and amphibians combined. Of the 28,000 identified species, 15,000 are marine dwelling. Because of this great diversity, fish are divided into three classes: Agnatha for jawless fish, Chondrichthyes for cartilaginous fish, and Osteichthyes for bony fish. All classes have three traits in common: they are aquatic, they have gills for breathing underwater, and they lack true limbs with digits.

Order: 59 orders total

Species: More than 15,000 marine fish (more than 28,000 total, including freshwater fish)

Size Range: 0.3 inch (8 millimeters), stout infantfish, to 41 feet (12.5 meters), whale shark

Weight Range: Less than 1 milligram, stout infantfish, to 41,000 pounds, whale shark

Distribution: All oceans worldwide

Habitat: From warm, tropical waters to cold, Arctic and Antarctic waters

Facts: Sharks are the only fish that have eyelids. The sailfish is the fastest fish in the ocean; it can swim at speeds of 68 miles (109 kilometers) per hour.

Fish Groups

Class Chondrichthyes (cartilaginous fish)

- Subclass Holocephali (Chimaeras)
- Subclass Elasmobranchii (sharks and rays)
  - Superorder Selachimorpha (sharks)
  - Superorder Batoidea (rays)

Superclass Osteichthyes (bony fish)

- Class Sarcopterygii (lobe-finned fish)
- Class Actinopterygii (ray-finned fish)

Superclass Agnatha (jawless fish)

- Order Myxiniformes (hagfish)
- Order Petromyzoniformes (lampreys)

Cartilaginous Fish

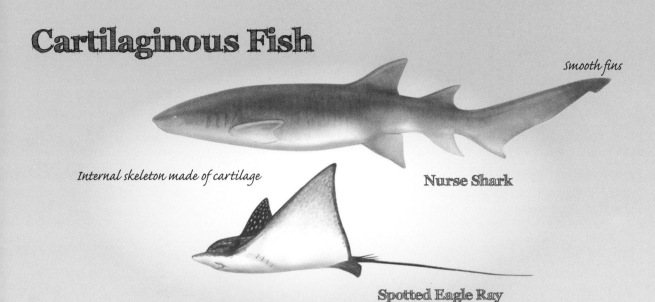

Smooth fins

Internal skeleton made of cartilage

Nurse Shark

Spotted Eagle Ray

Bony Fish

Lobe extending from body to form fin

Internal skeleton made of bone

Coelacanth

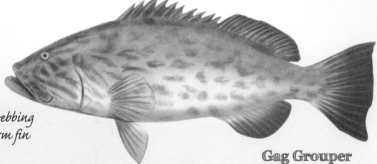

Bony spines, or rays, with webbing extending from body to form fin

Gag Grouper

Jawless Fish

Primitive with no paired fins

Sea Lamprey

Sharks

The Chondrichthyes class is comprised of fish with flexible internal skeletons formed of cartilage as opposed to bone. Chondrichthyes are covered in tiny scales called dermal denticles. They not only serve as armor to protect the fish, but also reduce drag in the water to make swimming more efficient. There are more than 1,000 species of Chondrichthyes.

Selachimorpha is represented by 500 species of sharks ranging in size from the lantern shark at 6.7 inches (17 centimeters) to the largest of all fish, the whale shark at more than 40 feet (12 meters). Unlike most animals, a shark's teeth are fixed to its gums, not its jaws, so sharks lose teeth regularly. New teeth are constantly replacing old or worn teeth and grow from the inside of the mouth and move outward in several rows. Sharks also have a developed sense of smell. Using their nostrils, some sharks can pick up scents (including blood) from as little as one part per million in seawater. That's equivalent to a drop of blood in a swimming pool.

First dorsal fin

Darkened fin tips

Second dorsal fin

Caudal fin

Eyes

Gill openings

Pectoral fin

Pelvic fin

Blacktip Shark
(Carcharhinus limbatus)
Found along coastal waters in tropical and subtropical climates worldwide, blacktip sharks mostly feed on fish, including rays and smaller sharks.
Length: 9 feet (2.7 meters)
Weight: 270 pounds
Conservation status: Near Threatened

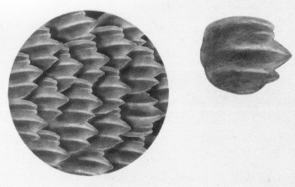

Enlarged detail of shark scales

Draw a
Great White

Use the blank grid below to draw what you see in each square at right. Feel free to add even more teeth!

Mackerel Sharks

The order of lamniform sharks, also called mackerel sharks, consists of some of the more familiar species, including the great white. Lamniformes typically have dark eyes and lack an eyelid. Instead, to protect their eyes from injury, they roll them back into their sockets, exposing the less vulnerable underside of the eyeball. They have generally large bodies with cone-shaped snouts, large gill openings, and mouths that extend past the eye. Many species of this order give birth to live young, and in some cases the embryos will feed on their siblings within the mother's womb prior to being born.

Blue-gray coloring on top of body

300 teeth arranged in rows are replaced when broken or worn down

White underside gives the great white shark its name

Did You Know?

Small pores on and around nose called ampullae of Lorenzini serve as electroreceptors to detect electrical fields emitted by fish.

Dorsal fin at middle of body

Long, torpedo-shaped body

Large pectoral fins

Tall dorsal fin

Great White Shark
(Carcharodon carcharias)

Found in temperate waters worldwide, great white sharks feed on marine mammals, including seals and small toothed whales, sea turtles, and fish.

Length: 20 feet (6 meters)
Weight: 4,300 pounds
Conservation status: Vulnerable

Large, crescent-shaped caudal fin helps the great white shark reach up to 25 miles (40 kilometers) per hour

Mackerel Sharks (continued)

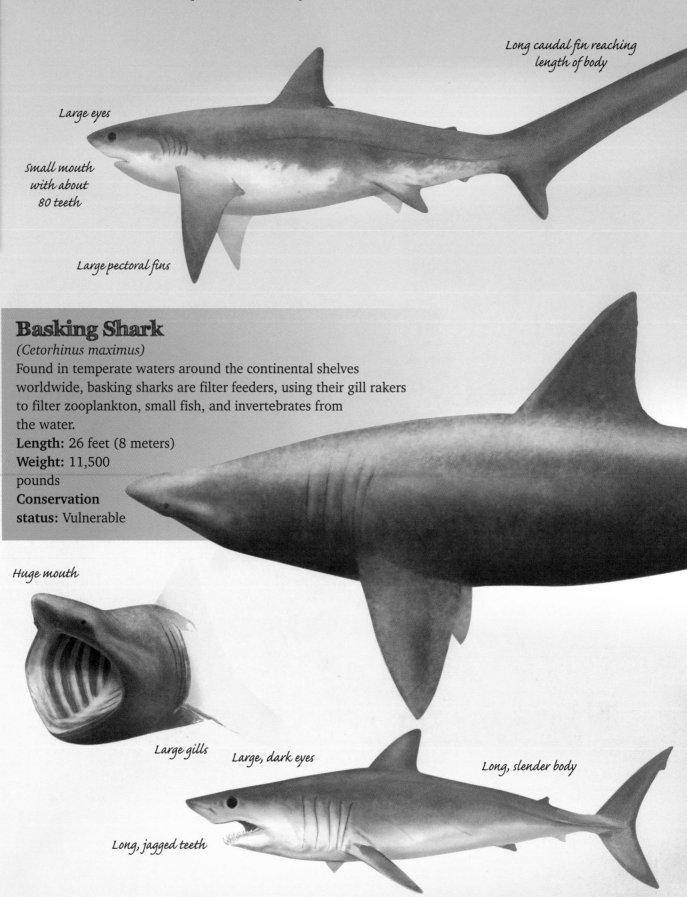

Long caudal fin reaching length of body

Large eyes

Small mouth with about 80 teeth

Large pectoral fins

Basking Shark
(*Cetorhinus maximus*)
Found in temperate waters around the continental shelves worldwide, basking sharks are filter feeders, using their gill rakers to filter zooplankton, small fish, and invertebrates from the water.
Length: 26 feet (8 meters)
Weight: 11,500 pounds
Conservation status: Vulnerable

Huge mouth

Large gills

Large, dark eyes

Long, slender body

Long, jagged teeth

Common Thresher Shark

(Alopias vulpinus)
Found in tropical and cold-temperate waters worldwide, common thresher sharks feed on small schooling fish.
Length: 20 feet (6 meters)
Weight: 4,300 pounds
Conservation status: Vulnerable

Massive caudal fin reaching 9 feet (2.7 meters) in height

smaller second dorsal fin

Shortfin Mako Shark

(Isurus oxyrinchus)
Found in temperate waters worldwide, shortfin mako sharks feed primarily on mackerels and tunas, but are known to also eat porpoises, sea turtles, and seabirds.
Length: 10 feet (3 meters)
Weight: 300 pounds
Conservation status: Vulnerable

Shark Bellies

Sharks are known for their aggressive behavior and big appetites. Many strange items have been found in the bellies of these big fish over the years—especially in great white and tiger sharks. Circle all the things you think have been found in the belly of a shark!

ANSWER ON PAGE 158

Carpet Sharks

Orectolobiformes, commonly called carpet sharks because of their ornately patterned skin, are a diverse group that differs greatly in appearance, size, and eating habits. All Orectolobiformes have relatively small eyes, a wide and short mouth that does not extend past their eyes, and two dorsal fins. They range in size from the 1-foot-long (30 centimeter) barbelthroat carpet shark to the 41-foot (12.5 meter) whale shark. With the exception of the whale shark, all Orectolobiformes have an opening behind the eye, called a spiracle, used for bottom feeding. Spiracles pump water from the top of the body downward into the gills to prevent sand from entering.

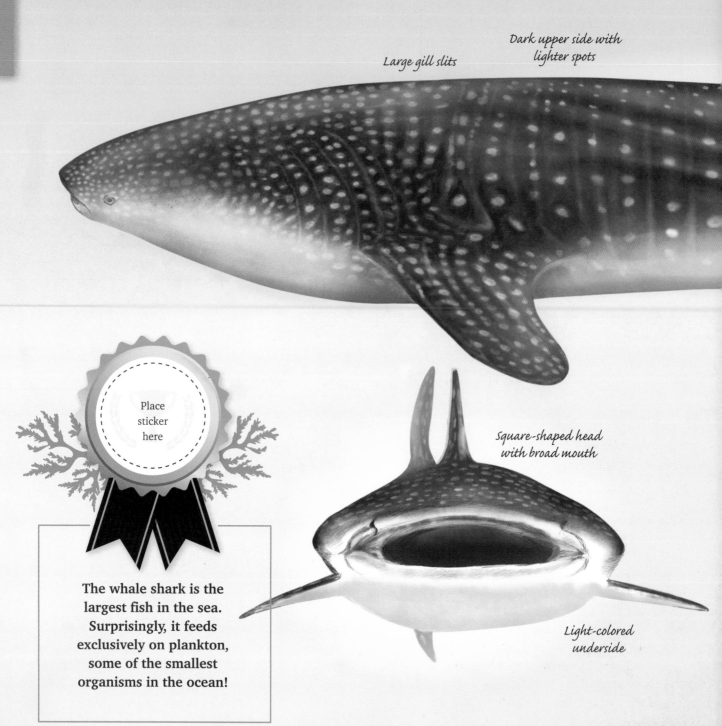

Large gill slits

Dark upper side with lighter spots

Place sticker here

Square-shaped head with broad mouth

Light-colored underside

The whale shark is the largest fish in the sea. Surprisingly, it feeds exclusively on plankton, some of the smallest organisms in the ocean!

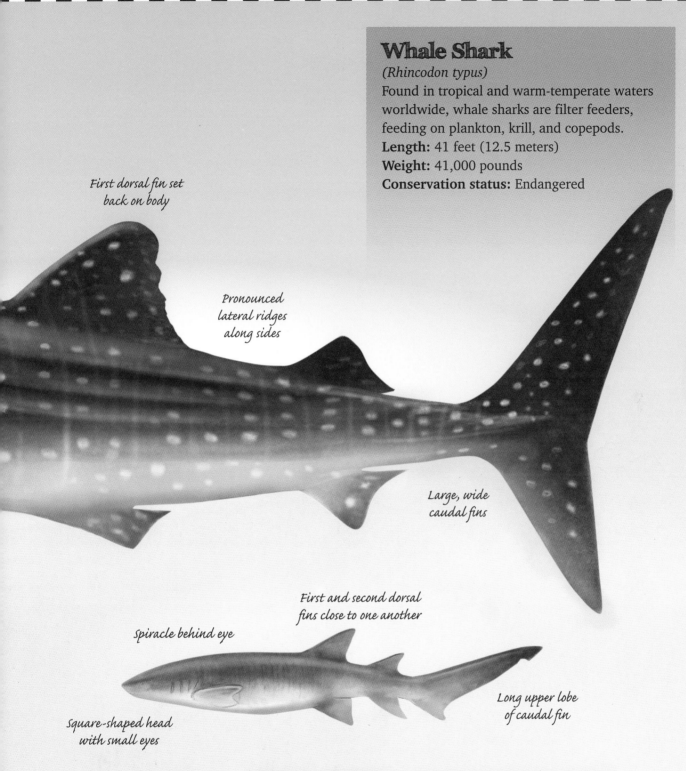

First dorsal fin set
back on body

Pronounced
lateral ridges
along sides

Large, wide
caudal fins

Whale Shark
(Rhincodon typus)
Found in tropical and warm-temperate waters
worldwide, whale sharks are filter feeders,
feeding on plankton, krill, and copepods.
Length: 41 feet (12.5 meters)
Weight: 41,000 pounds
Conservation status: Endangered

First and second dorsal
fins close to one another

Spiracle behind eye

Long upper lobe
of caudal fin

Square-shaped head
with small eyes

Nurse Shark
(Ginglymostoma cirratum)
Found along tropical and subtropical coastal waters of
the eastern Atlantic, western Atlantic, and eastern Pacific,
nurse sharks feed primarily on small fish, stingrays, and
small crustaceans.
Length: 10 feet (3 meters)
Weight: 330 pounds
Conservation status: Data Deficient

What Am I?

Test your detective instincts to figure out each animal below.
Find and place the matching stickers!

ANSWERS ON PAGE 158

Animal 1

I am a white animal who lives in the Arctic Circle.
I have a fluke but no dorsal fin! Some people call me
the "canary of the sea" because of the sounds I make.
What am I?

Place sticker here

Animal 2

I spend most of my time floating on my back. I have
whiskers, webbed feet, and a flattened tail. I'm known
for using stone tools to break open my food. What am I?

Place sticker here

Animal 3

I look like a manatee, but my tail looks like a
dolphin's fluke. I live in the Pacific Ocean and
primarily eat seagrass. What am I?

Place sticker here

Animal 4

I have a very impressive sense of smell and several
rows of sharp, triangular teeth that I use to bite my
prey. I have blue-gray coloring on the top of my body
and a white underside. What am I?

Place sticker here

Animal 5

When on land, I can walk on all fours. When in the
water, I use my rear flippers as a rudder. With large
foreflippers and a flexible body, I am a fluid, playful
swimmer. What am I?

Place sticker here

Name That Fin

Test your knowledge of sea animal anatomy.
Can you match each fin to its appropriate letter?

ANSWERS ON PAGE 158

White-Beaked Dolphin

A: Dorsal fin

B: Pectoral fin

C: Fluke

Great White Shark

A: First dorsal fin

B. Second dorsal fin

C: Pectoral fin

D: Pelvic fin

E. Caudal fin

Did You Know?

The common thresher shark (see pages 70-71) uses its long tail like a whip to strike and disable its prey.

Ground Sharks

The Carcharhiniform order contains the most species of sharks, numbering more than 200. Carcharhiniformes, commonly called ground sharks, are a vastly diverse group. They contain many recognizable species, including the tiger shark, the bull shark, and 10 species of hammerhead sharks. Carcharhiniformes all have nictitating membranes to protect their eyes, five gill openings, and two dorsal fins.

Bull Shark
(Carcharhinus leucas)

Found worldwide in coastal areas in warm waters, including freshwater lakes and rivers, bull sharks, also known as Zambezi sharks, are an aggressive species. They feed mostly on fish, sharks, rays, sea turtles, and terrestrial mammals.

Length: 11 feet (3.4 meters)
Weight: 290 pounds
Conservation status: Near Threatened

Large, triangular dorsal fin

Stocky, tall body

Did You Know?

Bull sharks are one of the few shark species capable of thriving in both saltwater and freshwater.

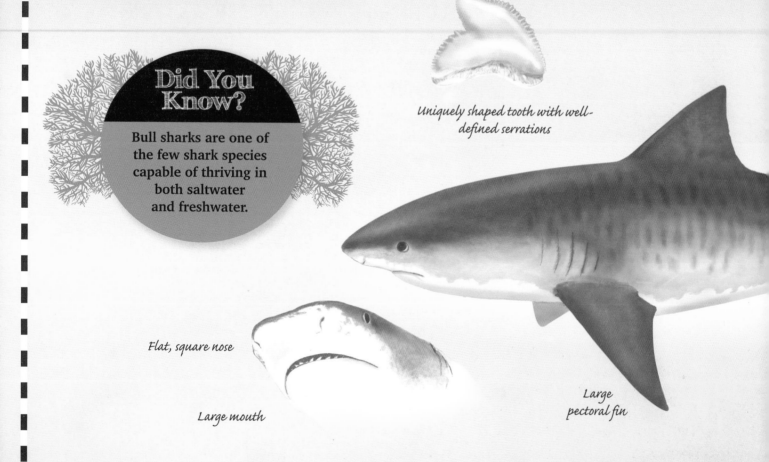

Uniquely shaped tooth with well-defined serrations

Flat, square nose

Large mouth

Large pectoral fin

Unique rounded fins with lighter tips

Round eyes with slitted pupils

Disproportionately long pectoral fins

Oceanic Whitetip Shark
(Carcharhinus longimanus)
Found in open oceans in temperate waters worldwide, oceanic whitetip sharks feed on varied schooling fish, squid, rays, sea turtles, and crustaceans.
Length: 10 feet (3 meters)
Weight: 200 pounds
Conservation status: Vulnerable

Striped pattern across body

Long upper lobe of caudal fin

Short lower lobe of caudal fin

Tiger Shark
(Galeocerdo cuvier)
Found in coastal areas in tropical and subtropical waters worldwide, tiger sharks are known for their broad diet and feed on almost anything, including marine mammals, sea turtles, other sharks, and rays.
Length: 16 feet (5 meters)
Weight: 1,400 pounds
Conservation status: Near Threatened

Small eyes at the ends of the head

Large, pronounced dorsal fin

Known for their unique flattened, U-shaped heads, hammerhead sharks are represented by 10 species

The wing-like structure on its head is called a cephalofoil

Small mouth designed for bottom feeding

Great Hammerhead Shark
(*Sphyrna mokarran*)
Found in tropical waters near coastlines worldwide, great hammerhead sharks have a varied diet of bony fish, crabs, lobsters, squid, smaller sharks, and stingrays.
Length: 20 feet (6 meters)
Weight: 1,200 pounds
Conservation status: Endangered

Broad and deep head shape

Spotted and striped pattern

First and second dorsal fins almost same size

Leopard Shark
(*Triakis semifasciata*)
Found in coastal areas in cool-to-warm waters in the northeastern Pacific Ocean, leopard sharks feed mostly on crabs, shrimp, and small bony fish.
Length: 6 feet (1.8 meters)
Weight: 40 pounds
Conservation status: Least Concern

Electrical Sensing Maze

The hammerhead shark's head is unique—and it's not just the shape! Its head has organs that detect electrical impulses, helping it track down prey. In the maze below, which path leads the shark to the squid dinner?

ANSWER ON PAGE 158

Rays

The superorder Batoidea is comprised of rays. Rays are closely related to sharks and are the largest group of cartilaginous fish, with more than 600 species. Physically, rays are distinguished by their flat bodies with oversized pectoral fins, which are used as a means of propulsion. Like sharks, bottom-dwelling batoids also have spiracle openings to aid in breathing when on the ocean floor. They range in size from the 4-inch (10-centimeter) short-nose electric ray to the 23-foot (7-meter) giant oceanic manta ray.

Myliobatiformes, commonly called stingrays, are one of four orders that make up Batoidea. There are more than 170 species of Myliobatiformes, many of which are equipped with barbed stingers protruding from their tails. These stingers are venomous and are used as a self-defensive weapon to elude attack.

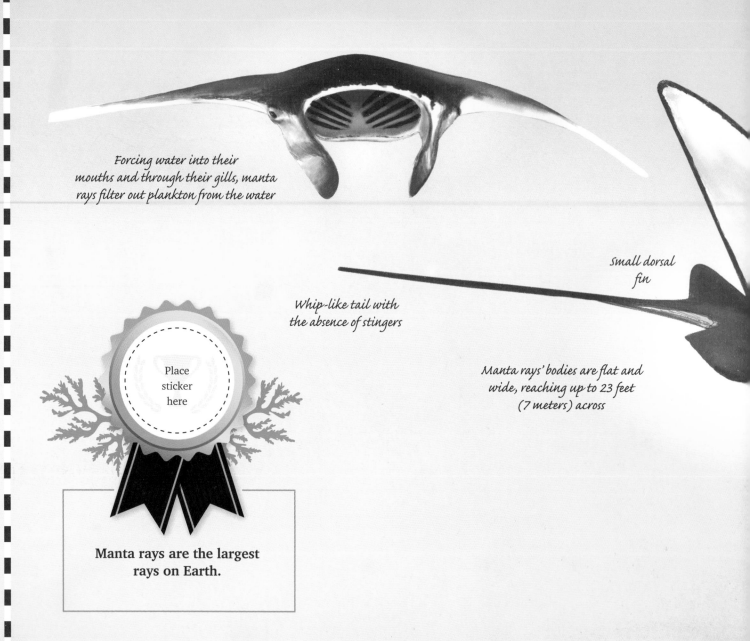

Forcing water into their mouths and through their gills, manta rays filter out plankton from the water

Small dorsal fin

Whip-like tail with the absence of stingers

Manta rays' bodies are flat and wide, reaching up to 23 feet (7 meters) across

Place sticker here

Manta rays are the largest rays on Earth.

Giant Oceanic Manta Ray

(Manta birostris)
Found in tropical and subtropical waters worldwide, manta rays, also called devil rays, are filter feeders that eat zooplankton, including krill.
Length: 23 feet (7 meters), wingspan
Weight: 2,900 pounds
Conservation status: Vulnerable

Ten gill slits on underside

Massive pectoral fins flap to propel the manta ray through the water

Light-colored or white underside

Small eyes

Two cephalic lobes direct plankton into the mouth

Southern Stingray

(Dasyatis americana)

Found in tropical and subtropical coastlines along the western Atlantic Ocean, southern stingrays forage the ocean floor to prey on small fish, worms, and crustaceans.

Length: 6 feet (1.8 meters), disc width
Weight: 215 pounds
Conservation status: Data Deficient

Did You Know?

Stingrays rely on their sensory organs, the ampullae of Lorenzini, to detect electrical fields emitted by their prey.

Southern stingrays can have multiple stingers

Ventral tail fin

Stingers have tiny, hooked barbs along two edges

Base

Bluespotted Ribbontail Ray

(Taeniura lymma)

Found in tropical waters in the Indo-Pacific region of the Indian Ocean, bluespotted ribbontail rays forage for small fish and various invertebrates.

Length: 14 inches (36 centimeters), disc width
Weight: 11 pounds
Conservation status: Near Threatened

Golden brown with blue spots

White underside

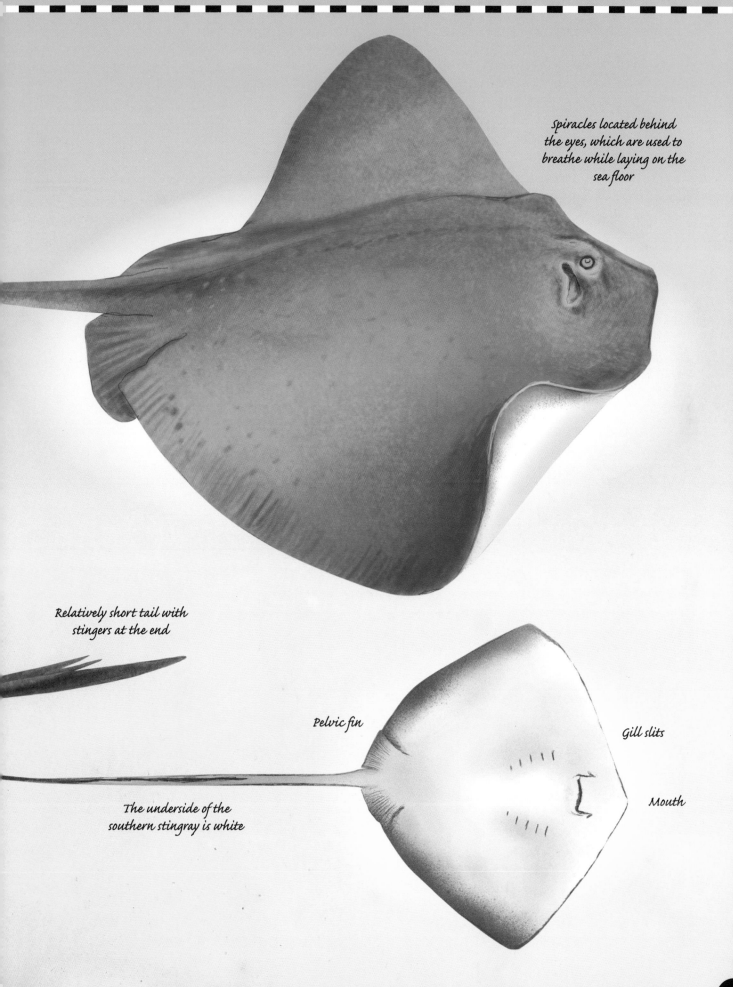

Spiracles located behind the eyes, which are used to breathe while laying on the sea floor

Relatively short tail with stingers at the end

Pelvic fin

Gill slits

Mouth

The underside of the southern stingray is white

Spotted Eagle Ray

(*Aetobatus narinari*)

Found in tropical, shallow, and coastal waters worldwide, spotted eagle rays feed on small invertebrates, including crabs, mollusks, shrimp, and octopuses.

Length: 16 feet (5 meters), including tail; 10 feet (3 meters), wingspan

Weight: 500 pounds

Conservation status: Near Threatened

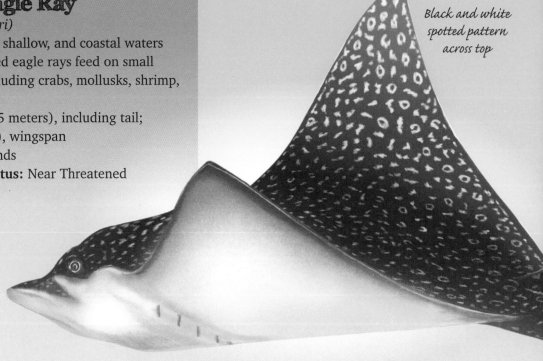

Black and white spotted pattern across top

Sawfish

Pristiforms, or sawfish, are an order of Batoidea characterized by a long, flattened nose called a rostrum, with teeth-like structures called denticles projecting from the sides. The rostrum is covered in tiny pores that detect movement from their prey buried in the sand. There are a total of six sawfish species.

Tooth-like denticles project outward horizontally from snout, as seen in this overhead view of the head

Spiracles

Eyes

Broad, flat nose reaching more than 6 feet (1.8 meters) long

Mouth and gills on underside

Large and flat pectoral fins

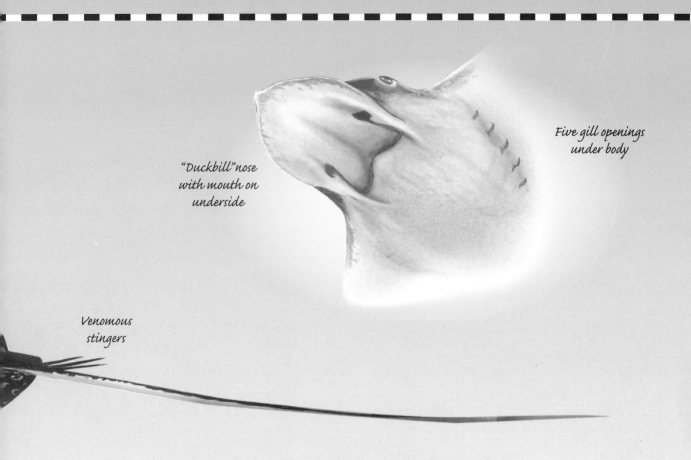

"Duckbill" nose with mouth on underside

Five gill openings under body

Venomous stingers

Smalltooth Sawfish
(Pristis pectinata)
Found in tropical, shallow, and coastal waters worldwide, smalltooth sawfish use their long, toothed noses to dig up crustaceans and mollusks, and to strike schools of fish.
Length: 20 feet (6 meters)
Weight: 800 pounds
Conservation status: Critically Endangered

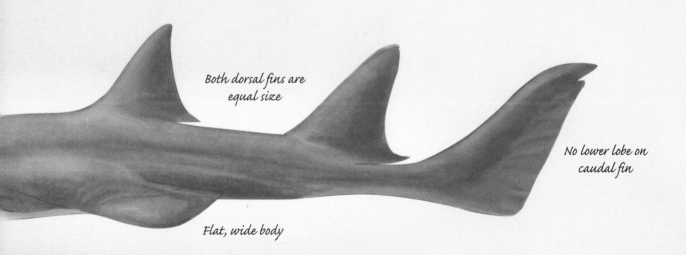

Both dorsal fins are equal size

No lower lobe on caudal fin

Flat, wide body

Rays of Color

Rays are generally brown or gray in color to help them blend in with the sea floor. You can color this collection of rays accurately with neutrals, or you can have fun and choose much bolder colors!

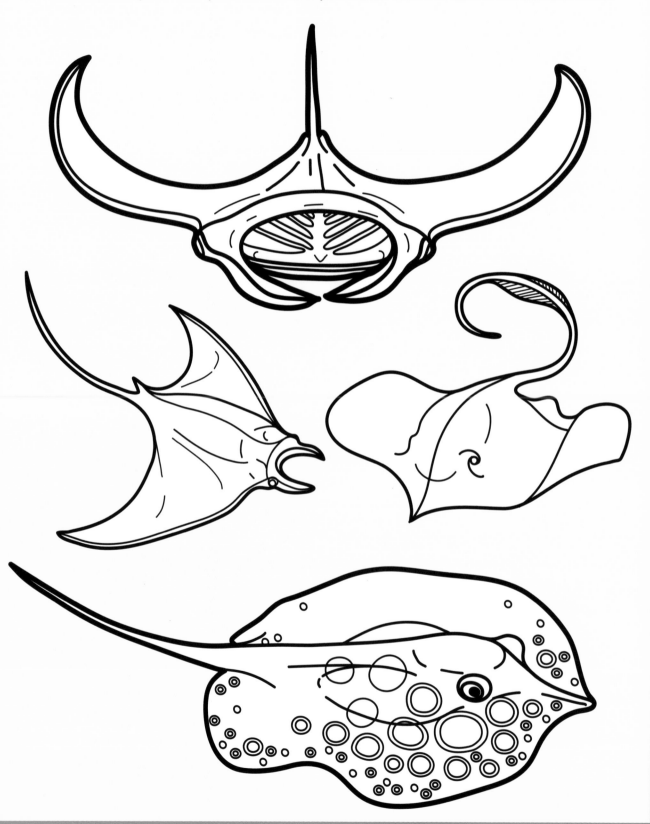

Sharks & Rays Crossword

Fill in the blanks below and use the numbers to enter the words into the crossword puzzle.

ANSWERS ON PAGE 158

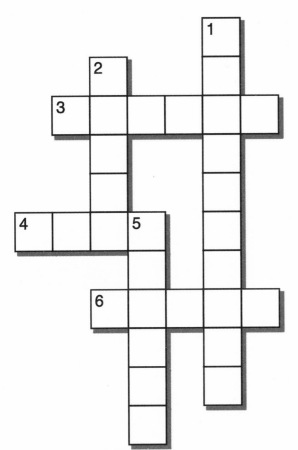

Down

1. Bull sharks are capable of thriving in both saltwater and _____ environments.

2. On stingrays, the ____ are located under the body.

5. The great white shark has dark eyes that lack an _____.

Across

3. The basking shark is a _____ feeder, meaning that it uses its gill rakers to collect food from the water.

4. Sawfish have a long, flattened _____ called a rostrum, with teeth-like structures along the side.

6. Sharks have rows of _____ that are constantly being replaced.

True or False?

Stingrays use their barbed, venomous stingers as tools for capturing their prey.

ANSWER ON PAGE 158

Lobe-Finned Fish

Osteichthyes are a superclass of fish that have a bony skeleton and an internal organ called a swim bladder. Swim bladders are gas-filled sacs that are used to control the fish's ability to float. Osteichthyes also have a system of sensory organs called a lateral line, which can be seen as a horizontal line running along the length of the body. Lateral lines are used to detect vibration, movement, and pressure changes in the water around the fish. Osteichthyes consist of two main groups: Sarcopterygii for lobe-finned fish and Actinopterygii for ray-finned fish.

Lobe-finned fish, the fish in the Sarcopterygii class, have a fleshy lobe extending from the body, forming the fins. There are only eight remaining species of this class: two species of coelacanths and six species of freshwater lungfish. Many scientists believe the ancestors of modern Sarcopterygii species played an important role in the transition from sea-based animals to land-based animals.

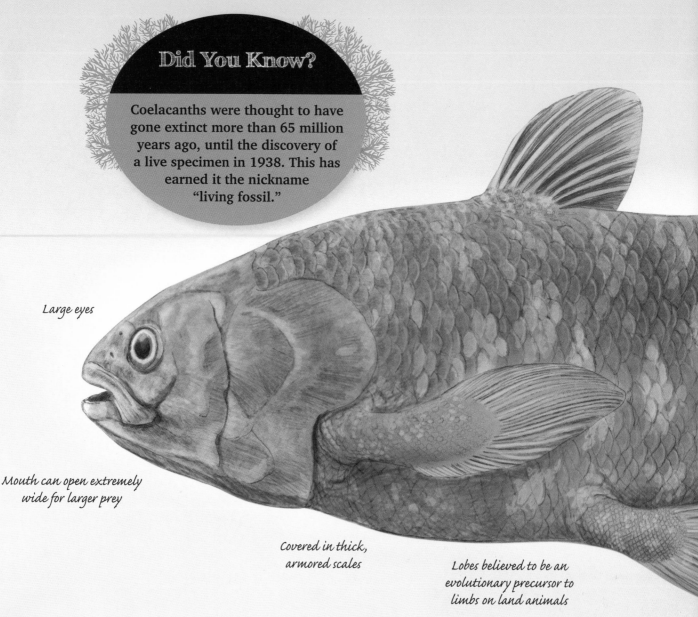

Did You Know?

Coelacanths were thought to have gone extinct more than 65 million years ago, until the discovery of a live specimen in 1938. This has earned it the nickname "living fossil."

Large eyes

Mouth can open extremely wide for larger prey

Covered in thick, armored scales

Lobes believed to be an evolutionary precursor to limbs on land animals

Spot the Difference

There are three differences between these two fish. Can you find them all?

ANSWER ON PAGE 158

West Indian Ocean Coelacanth

(Latimeria chalumnae)

Found in water from 100 to 500 meters deep off the coast of east Africa, west Indian Ocean coelacanths feed mostly on cuttlefish, squid, octopuses, and small fish.

Length: 6.5 feet (2 meters)
Weight: 200 pounds
Conservation status: Critically Endangered

Three-lobed tail is unique to coelacanths

Paired pectoral and pelvic fins move in a walking-like way when swimming

Tarpon & Ladyfish

The fish in the Actinopterygii class are known for having bony spines, or rays, with a web of skin forming their fins. They are by far the largest class of fish, containing 99 percent of all fish species.

The Elopiform order of fish is comprised of two genera and a total of nine species of tarpon and ladyfish. All species are capable of living in both fresh water and salt water. They will pass from one to the other regularly. Elopiformes are primitive and have an open duct in their swim bladders used like a lung. This requires them to take gulps of air from the surface and gives them the advantage of living in waters with low oxygen levels to avoid being hunted by larger fish when young.

Taller upper lobe on caudal fin

Atlantic Tarpon

(*Megalops atlanticus*)
Found in tropical and subtropical regions of the Atlantic Ocean, as well as freshwater lakes and rivers, Atlantic tarpon feed on small fish and various crustaceans.
Length: 8 feet (2.4 meters)
Weight: 355 pounds
Conservation status: Vulnerable

Tarpons are covered in large, thick, silvery scales

Mouth angled upward to take in air from the surface and feed on surface-dwelling fish

Thick, tubular body

Sturgeons

Acipenseriformes, an order of fish represented by 27 species of sturgeons and paddlefish, are among the oldest families of fish. Their skeletons are primarily cartilaginous, like those of sharks, but they have a bony skull, jaws, and rays supporting the fins. All species of Acipenseriformes are bottom-feeders with adaptations for finding and securing prey hidden in sand. One of these adaptations are barbels, which are small appendages that dangle from their noses. The barbels act as sensory organs to feel and taste prey that cannot be easily seen.

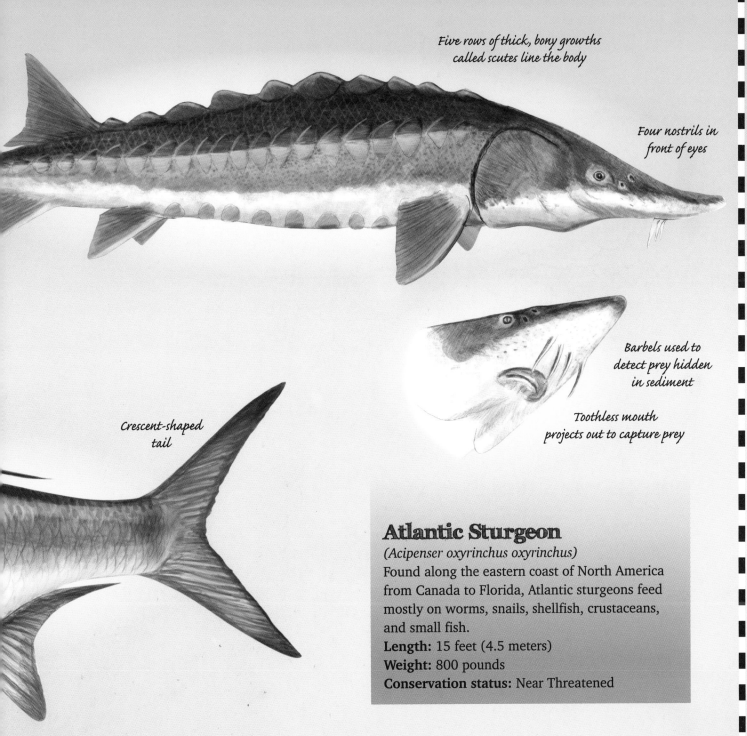

Five rows of thick, bony growths called scutes line the body

Four nostrils in front of eyes

Barbels used to detect prey hidden in sediment

Toothless mouth projects out to capture prey

Crescent-shaped tail

Atlantic Sturgeon
(Acipenser oxyrinchus oxyrinchus)
Found along the eastern coast of North America from Canada to Florida, Atlantic sturgeons feed mostly on worms, snails, shellfish, crustaceans, and small fish.
Length: 15 feet (4.5 meters)
Weight: 800 pounds
Conservation status: Near Threatened

Marine Eels

The Anguilliformes order is made up of about 800 species of eels, with most being predators. Many eel species begin their lives in fresh water and later make their way into the ocean. Eels can be easily distinguished by their long ribbon-like bodies that lack pelvic and caudal fins. Some marine eels, like the moray eels, have developed specialized adaptations for hunting prey. Morays have a second set of jaws and teeth called a pharyngeal jaw. This jaw is located in the eel's throat. When attacking prey, it juts out to grab and pull its prey into its throat. Anguilliformes range in size from the 2-inch-long (5-centimeter) one-jawed eel to the 13-foot-long (4-meter) giant moray.

Zebra Moray Eel

(*Gymnomuraena zebra*)
Found throughout the Indo-Pacific area from the eastern coast of Africa to the western coast of America, zebra morays feed mainly on fish, clams, squid, scallops, and shrimp.
Length: 5 feet (1.5 meters)
Weight: 20 pounds
Conservation status: Data Deficient

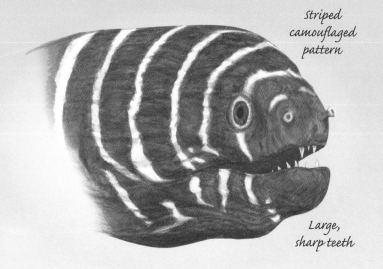

Striped camouflaged pattern

Large, sharp teeth

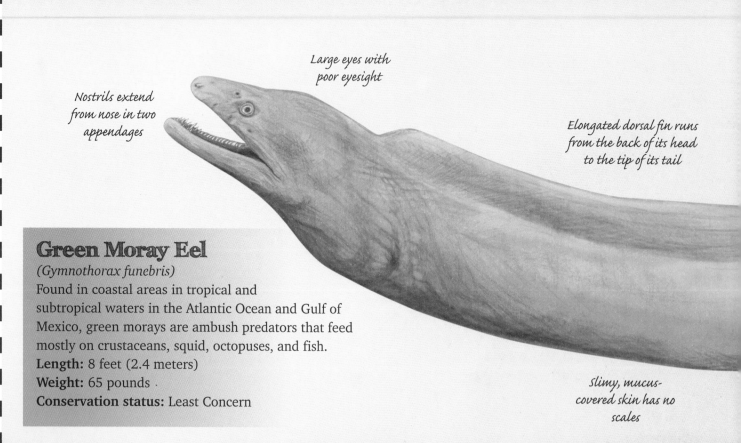

Large eyes with poor eyesight

Nostrils extend from nose in two appendages

Elongated dorsal fin runs from the back of its head to the tip of its tail

Green Moray Eel

(*Gymnothorax funebris*)
Found in coastal areas in tropical and subtropical waters in the Atlantic Ocean and Gulf of Mexico, green morays are ambush predators that feed mostly on crustaceans, squid, octopuses, and fish.
Length: 8 feet (2.4 meters)
Weight: 65 pounds
Conservation status: Least Concern

Slimy, mucus-covered skin has no scales

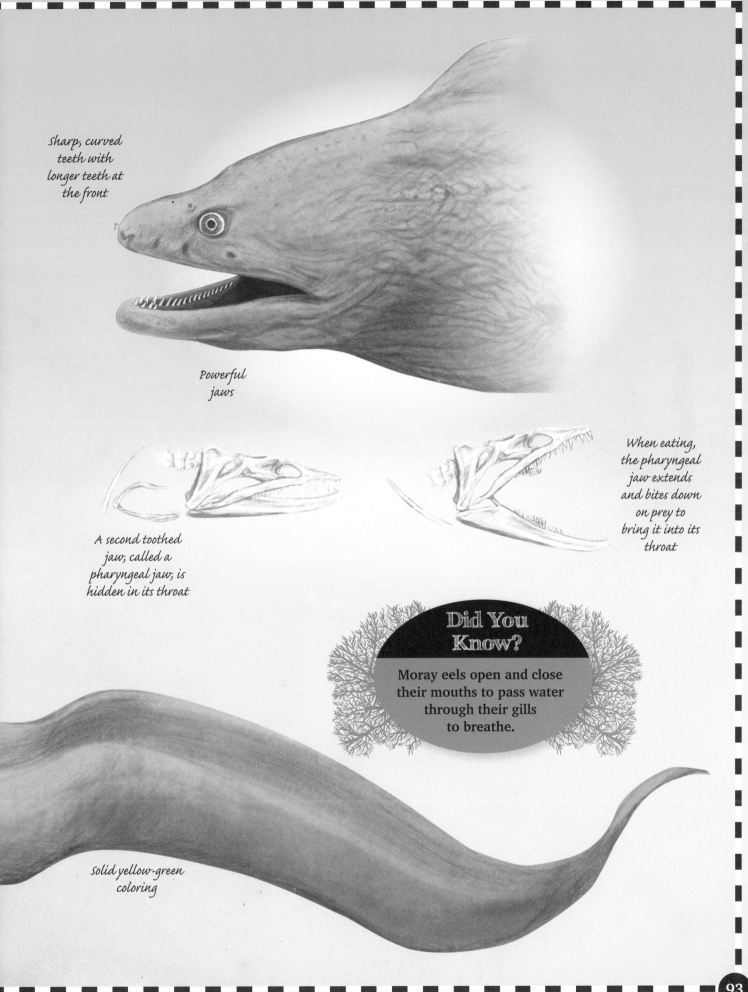

Sharp, curved teeth with longer teeth at the front

Powerful jaws

A second toothed jaw, called a pharyngeal jaw, is hidden in its throat

When eating, the pharyngeal jaw extends and bites down on prey to bring it into its throat

Did You Know?

Moray eels open and close their mouths to pass water through their gills to breathe.

Solid yellow-green coloring

Boxfishes, Triggerfishes & Ocean Sunfish

The Tetraodontiformes order of fish is represented by more than 300 species in varying shapes and sizes. Departing from the usual streamlined shape of most fish, Tetraodontiformes range from square to round to flat. Some, like the puffer fish, can even change their shape by inflating with water. Tetraodontiformes range in size from the ¾-inch (2-centimeter) diamond leatherjacket fish to the 10-foot (3.3-meter) ocean sunfish.

Colorful markings

Small mouth can crush shells

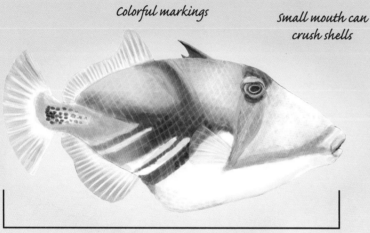

Picasso Triggerfish
(Rhinecanthus aculeatus)

10 inches (25 centimeters), 1 pound

Small mouth is low on the body

Eats small organisms from the ocean floor

Longhorn Cowfish
(Lactoria cornuta)

20 inches (51 centimeters), 6 ounces

Toxins in the body make it poisonous

Feeds mostly on corals

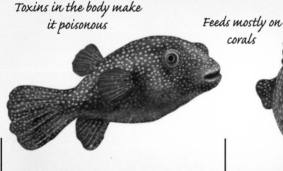

Guineafowl Puffer Fish
(Arothron meleagris)

20 inches (51 centimeters), 1 pound

Deters predators by inflating to more than twice its normal size

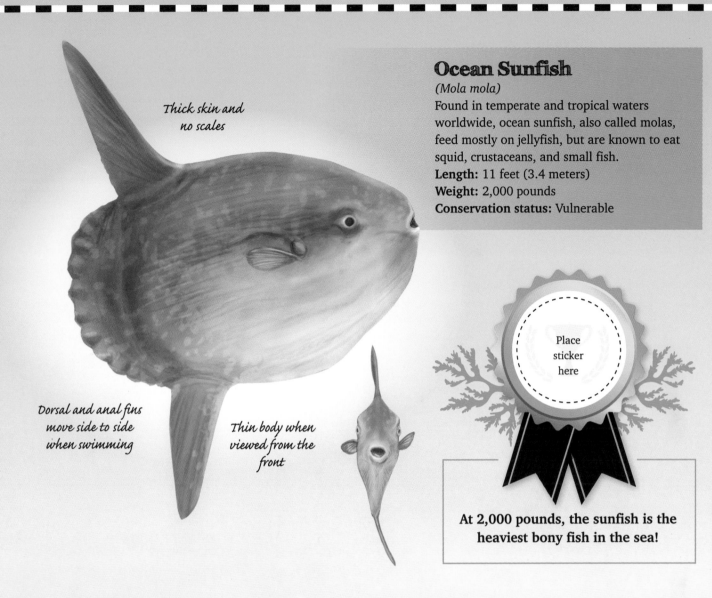

Ocean Sunfish
(Mola mola)

Found in temperate and tropical waters worldwide, ocean sunfish, also called molas, feed mostly on jellyfish, but are known to eat squid, crustaceans, and small fish.

Length: 11 feet (3.4 meters)
Weight: 2,000 pounds
Conservation status: Vulnerable

Thick skin and no scales

Dorsal and anal fins move side to side when swimming

Thin body when viewed from the front

Place sticker here

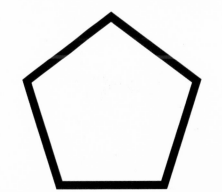

At 2,000 pounds, the sunfish is the heaviest bony fish in the sea!

Create a Fish!

The Tetraodontiformes order contains fish of different shapes and sizes, some of which are very unusual. Draw on the shapes to the right to create your own fish!

My fish is called _____.

My fish eats _____.

My fish is _____ inches/centimeters long

and weighs _____ pounds.

My fish is unique because _____

_____.

Opahs & Oarfish

The Lampriformes order consists of 20 species of fish, all of which are pelagic, meaning they live in the open ocean far above the ocean floor. They live in water ranging from 300 (91 meters) to more than 3,000 feet (914 meters) deep. Lampriformes have flat-sided bodies either elongated or circular in shape. They range in size from the 12-inch (30-centimeter) sailfin moonfish to the longest of all bony fish, the 36-foot (11-meter) giant oarfish.

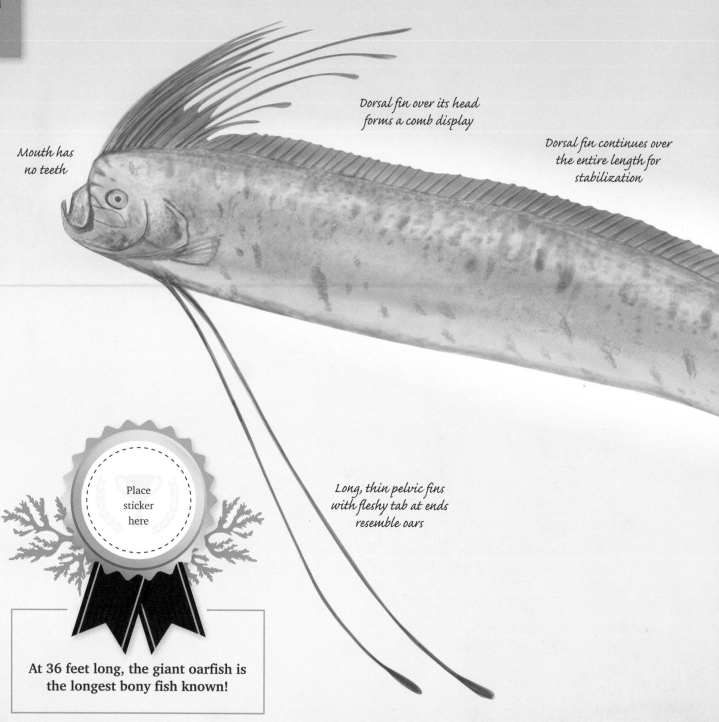

Dorsal fin over its head forms a comb display

Dorsal fin continues over the entire length for stabilization

Mouth has no teeth

Long, thin pelvic fins with fleshy tab at ends resemble oars

Place sticker here

At 36 feet long, the giant oarfish is the longest bony fish known!

Opah

(Lampris guttatus)
Found worldwide in subtropical and temperate waters, opahs, commonly known as moonfish, feed mostly on krill and squid.
Length: 6.5 feet (2 meters)
Weight: 600 pounds
Conservation status: Least Concern

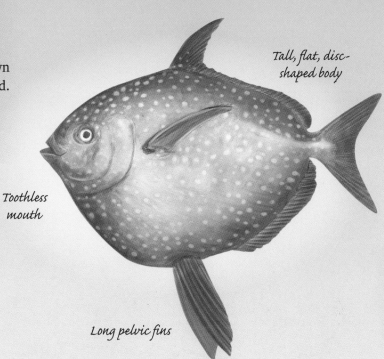

Tall, flat, disc-shaped body

Toothless mouth

Long pelvic fins

Opahs are one of the few warm-blooded fish, meaning they can regulate their own body temperature

Giant Oarfish

(Regalecus glesne)
Found worldwide in subtropical waters, giant oarfish, also called ribbonfish, feed on krill as well as small fish and squid.
Length: 36 feet (11 meters)
Weight: 600 pounds
Conservation status: Least Concern

Use your stickers to fill this deep blue ocean with life!

Cods & Haddocks

The Gadiform order of fish is made up of more than 180 species and includes many fish that are commonly consumed by humans, such as cod. Gadiformes mainly live in temperate to cold waters in large schools and feed on smaller fish and crustaceans, including crabs, from the sea floor. They are diverse in size, from the 2.8-inch (7-centimeter) codlet to the 6-foot (2-meter) Atlantic cod.

Atlantic Cod

(Gadus morhua)
Found in the northwestern Atlantic through the Arctic Ocean, Atlantic cod feed primarily on crustaceans and schooling fish.
Length: 6.5 feet (2 meters)
Weight: 200 pounds
Conservation status: Vulnerable

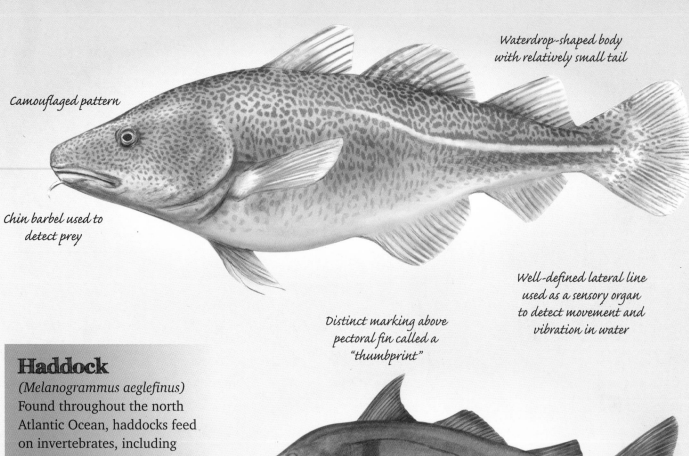

Waterdrop-shaped body with relatively small tail

Camouflaged pattern

Chin barbel used to detect prey

Well-defined lateral line used as a sensory organ to detect movement and vibration in water

Distinct marking above pectoral fin called a "thumbprint"

Haddock

(Melanogrammus aeglefinus)
Found throughout the north Atlantic Ocean, haddocks feed on invertebrates, including crustaceans and mollusks, while some larger individuals will feed on small fish.
Length: 2.3 feet (70 centimeters)
Weight: 4 pounds
Conservation status: Vulnerable

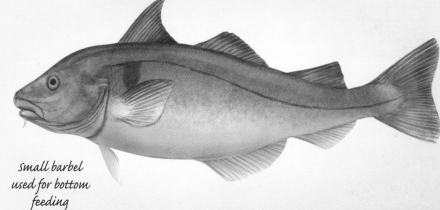

small barbel used for bottom feeding

Spot the Different Cod

Atlantic cod like to travel in large schools of fish. On this page, one of these fish is not like the others! Can you spot it?

ANSWER ON PAGE 158

Gurnards & Lionfish

The Scorpaeniformes order is one of the largest orders of fish, consisting of more than 1,300 species. Scorpaeniformes are generally small, averaging about 12 inches (30 centimeters) in length, with most species being bottom-dwellers.

Strong spines

Large, bony plates on head

Separated rays of pectoral fins used to feel for prey in the sand

Large, wing-like pectoral fins

Red Gurnard

(Chelidonichthys cuculus)
Found in the Northwest Pacific Ocean, red gurnards feed mostly on crabs, shrimp, small fish, and worms.
Length: 20 inches (51 centimeters)
Weight: 4.4 pounds
Conservation status: Least Concern

Nonvenomous, long, expansive pectoral fins

Did You Know?

Some rockfish and lionfish have developed venomous spines as a means of self-defense. Small glands within their needle-like spines produce a strong venom that can give the attacker a painful wound.

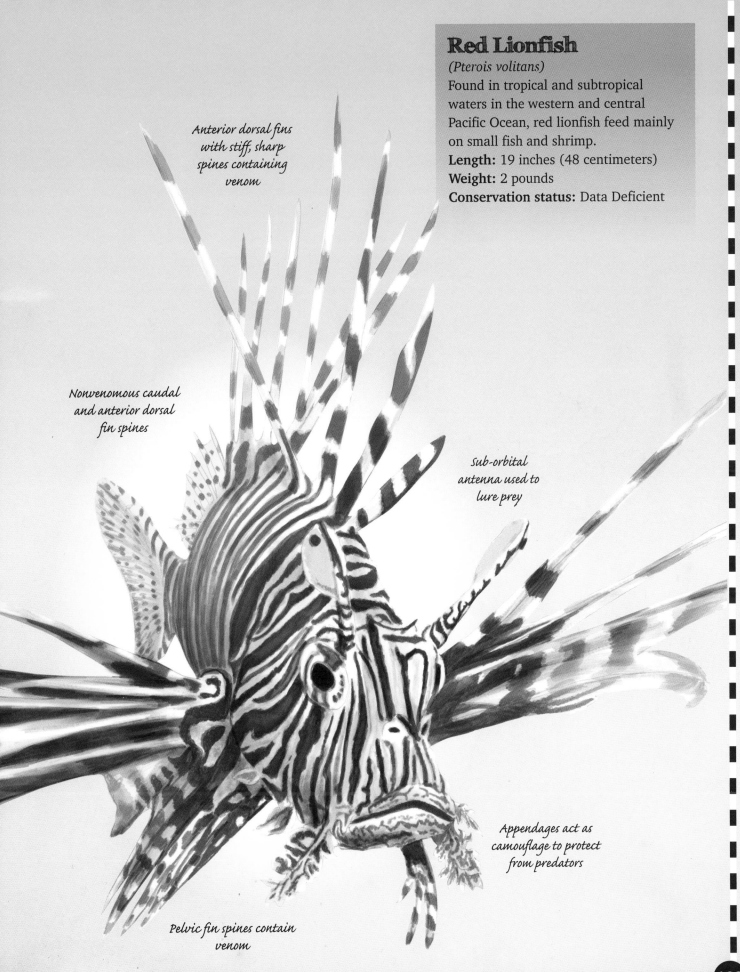

Anterior dorsal fins
with stiff, sharp
spines containing
venom

Red Lionfish
(Pterois volitans)
Found in tropical and subtropical
waters in the western and central
Pacific Ocean, red lionfish feed mainly
on small fish and shrimp.
Length: 19 inches (48 centimeters)
Weight: 2 pounds
Conservation status: Data Deficient

Nonvenomous caudal
and anterior dorsal
fin spines

Sub-orbital
antenna used to
lure prey

Appendages act as
camouflage to protect
from predators

Pelvic fin spines contain
venom

Flatfish

Fish from the Pleuronectiform order, also called flatfish, are easily recognizable. Young flatfish start out looking like most other fish but go through a developmental metamorphosis during which their eyes migrate to one side of their bodies. Once this takes place, they spend the rest of their lives on the ocean floor, where they feed on bottom-dwelling animals and hide from predators.

Eyes both on one side

Mouth oriented vertically

Atlantic Halibut
(Hippoglossus hippoglossus)

Dorsal and anal fins of equal height

Slight fork in caudal fin

15 feet (4.5 meters), 700 pounds

Disc-shaped body with smaller head than halibut

Did You Know?

Some species of flatfish have eyes on the right side of their bodies (called dextral), others on the left side (called sinistral), and some species have a combination of orientations.

2.3 feet (70 centimeters), 8 pounds

Underside is pale with no markings

Winter Flounder
(Pseudopleuronectes americanus)

Flying Fish, Halfbeaks & Needlefish

The Beloniformes order is made up of relatively small fish totaling more than 300 species. Beloniformes generally have elongated bodies with large eyes and their dorsal fins set far back, toward their tails.

Bennett's Flying Fish

(*Cheilopogon pinnatibarbatus*)
Found in tropical and subtropical waters across the Pacific Ocean, Bennett's flying fish feed exclusively on plankton.
Length: 15 inches (38 centimeters)
Weight: 1.3 pounds
Conservation status: Least Concern

Flying fish are capable of reaching speeds of more than 35 miles (56 kilometers) per hour

Flying fish can jump out from the surface and glide through the air to flee predators

Much longer lower jaw

American Halfbeak

(*Hyporhamphus meeki*)

7 inches (17.8 centimeters), 150 grams

Atlantic Needlefish

(*Strongylura marina*)

Long, slender build

Large eyes

Elongated jaws with thin, narrow teeth for grasping prey

3.3 feet (1 meter), 5 pounds

Seahorses & Seadragons

Syngnathiformes are recognizable due to their long snouts with small mouths at the ends. Most live in and around seaweed, which they use to evade predators. Syngnathiformes are mostly small and include seahorses, seadragons, pipefish, and trumpetfish.

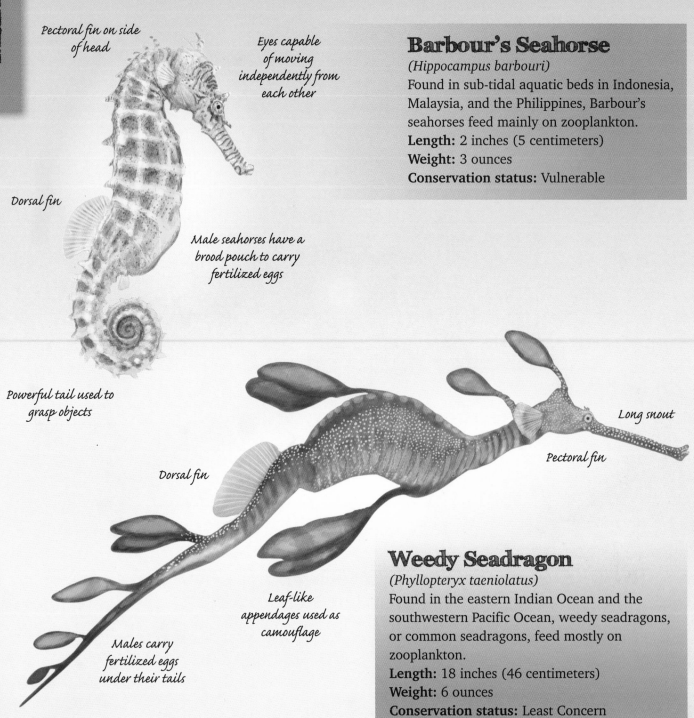

Pectoral fin on side of head

Eyes capable of moving independently from each other

Dorsal fin

Male seahorses have a brood pouch to carry fertilized eggs

Powerful tail used to grasp objects

Long snout

Pectoral fin

Dorsal fin

Leaf-like appendages used as camouflage

Males carry fertilized eggs under their tails

Barbour's Seahorse

(*Hippocampus barbouri*)
Found in sub-tidal aquatic beds in Indonesia, Malaysia, and the Philippines, Barbour's seahorses feed mainly on zooplankton.
Length: 2 inches (5 centimeters)
Weight: 3 ounces
Conservation status: Vulnerable

Weedy Seadragon

(*Phyllopteryx taeniolatus*)
Found in the eastern Indian Ocean and the southwestern Pacific Ocean, weedy seadragons, or common seadragons, feed mostly on zooplankton.
Length: 18 inches (46 centimeters)
Weight: 6 ounces
Conservation status: Least Concern

Seahorse Dot-to-Dot

Starting at number 1, connect the dots in order with a pen or pencil. Then use markers, colored pencils, or crayons to color in your seahorse!

Anglerfish

Lophiiformes, better known as anglerfish, have a unique hunting method. They create light to lure fish within reach to swallow. One group, the deep sea anglers, live in the Bathypelagic and Abyssopelagic zones of the ocean, where there is no light. They must rely on bioluminescence, or self-generating light, as a means to lure their prey. There are 322 species in the Lophiiform order.

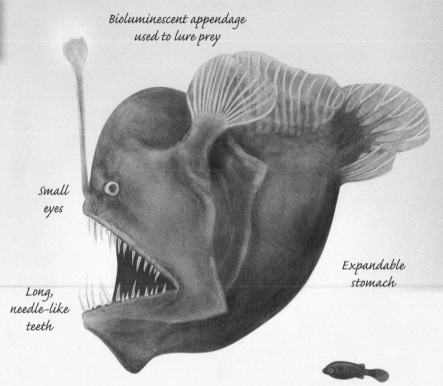

Bioluminescent appendage used to lure prey

Small eyes

Long, needle-like teeth

Expandable stomach

The male humpback anglerfish is only a fraction of the size of the female

Humpback Anglerfish

(Melanocetus johnsonii)
Found in depths up to 14,700 feet (4,500 meters) in oceans worldwide, humpback anglerfish can feed on fish close to their own size.
Length: Females are 7 inches (17.5 centimeters), males are 1 inch (2.5 centimeters)
Conservation status: Least Concern

Bufoceratias shaoi

(Bufoceratias shaoi)
Found in the western Pacific and Indian Oceans at depths up to 4,000 feet (1,200 meters), Bufoceratias shaoi lacks a common name, and very little is known about this species. They feed primarily on fish and squid.
Length: 4 inches (10 centimeters)
Conservation status: Data Deficient

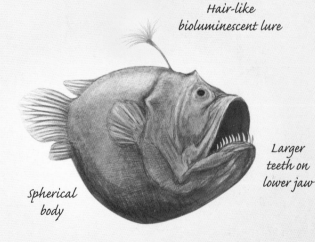

Hair-like bioluminescent lure

Larger teeth on lower jaw

Spherical body

Pelican Eels

The Saccopharyngiformes order consists of a small group of odd, eel-like fish that live in water as deep as 10,000 feet (3,000 meters). Most are known for their loosely hinged, enormous mouths that let them swallow fish close to their own size. Their teeth are remarkably small compared to their mouths. Saccopharyngiformes have typically scaleless, smooth skin and use their long dorsal fin for balance when hunting. There are 28 known species in the saccopharyngiform order.

Pelican Eel
(Eurypharynx pelecanoides)
Found in all oceans worldwide at 9,800 feet deep (3,000 meters), pelican eels, sometimes called gulper eels, feed mostly on zooplankton consisting of small crustaceans, but they are capable of eating squid and large fish as well.

Length: 30 inches (76 centimeters)

Conservation status: Least Concern

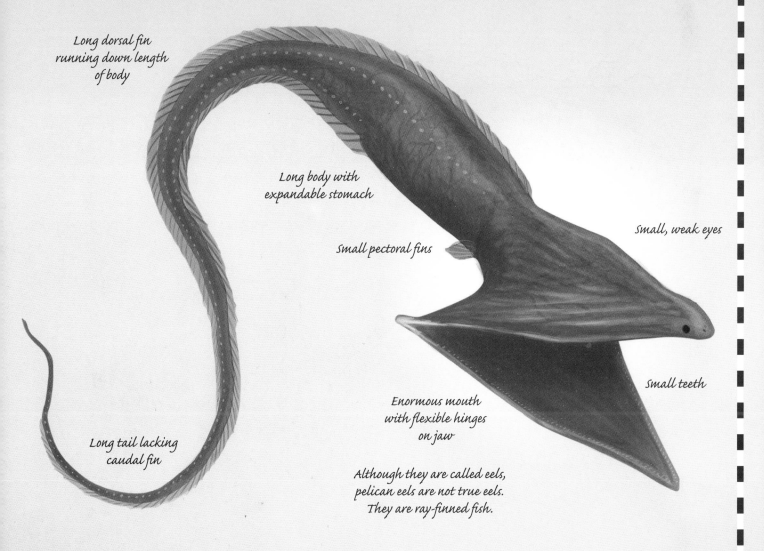

Long dorsal fin running down length of body

Long body with expandable stomach

Small pectoral fins

Small, weak eyes

Small teeth

Long tail lacking caudal fin

Enormous mouth with flexible hinges on jaw

Although they are called eels, pelican eels are not true eels. They are ray-finned fish.

Marine Fish Crossword

Use the knowledge you've gained about marine fish to fill in the crossword.

ANSWERS ON PAGE 158

Down

1. Cartilaginous fish have internal skeletons made of _____.

2. Fish have _____ for swimming underwater.

4. The largest ray on Earth is the _____ ray.

Across

3. The fastest fish in the ocean is the _____.

4. Fish have been around for more than 450 _____ years.

5. Anglerfish have long, needle-like _____ in their mouths.

Mysteries of the Deep

Use the code below to discover something about the mysterious ocean!

ANSWERS ON PAGE 158

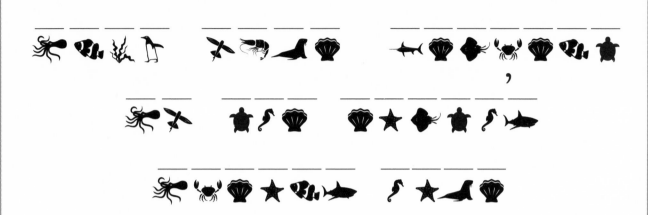

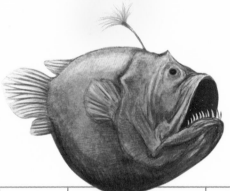

★	🐟	🦀	🐬	🐚		🪸	🌊	🦐
A	B	C	D	E	F	G	H	I

🪼	🦈	🌿	🐬	🐠	🐙		🦞	
J	K	L	M	N	O	P	Q	R

🦈	🐢		🦭	🐋	🦞	🐧	🐟	
S	T	U	V	W	X	Y	Z

Perciformes

The perciform order is the largest order of vertebrates on Earth, containing more than 10,000 species (about 8,000 are marine), or 41 percent of all bony fish (Osteichthyes superclass). Perciformes are a highly successful group, diverse in size, diet, and habitat, living in all areas of the oceans from shorelines to deep sea. Many popular aquarium fish, such as clownfish and butterflyfish, are Perciformes, as are tuna, swordfish, and groupers.

Metallic green-blue stripes with silver underside

small finlets

Atlantic Mackerel
(Scomber scombrus)

2 feet (61 centimeters), 7 pounds

First and second dorsal fins fused together

The endangered nassau grouper can quickly change color to avoid predators

Nassau Grouper
(Epinephelus striatus)

Large mouth to swallow prey whole

4 feet (1.2 meters), 50 pounds

Small teeth lining the jaw, tongue, and roof of mouth

Cobia
(Rachycentron canadum)

Two light-colored markings run length of body

Broad snout with protruding lower jaw

6.5 feet (2 meters), 170 pounds

Great Barracuda

(Sphyraena barracuda)

Found from mangroves and reefs to open-water environments in the Indian, Pacific, and Atlantic Oceans, great barracudas, also called giant barracudas, are ambush predators that feed primarily on smaller fish.

Length: 5 feet (1.5 meters)

Weight: 100 pounds

Conservation status: Least Concern

Broad caudal fin

Can swim short bursts up to 27 miles (24 kilometers) per hour

Draw a Barracuda

The barracuda has a pointed, streamlined nose; large, sharp front teeth; and small back teeth. Use the blank grid below to draw what you see in each square at right.

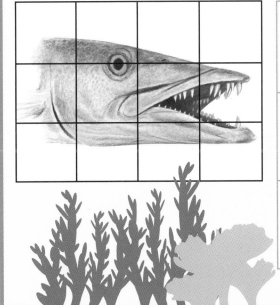

Perciformes (continued)

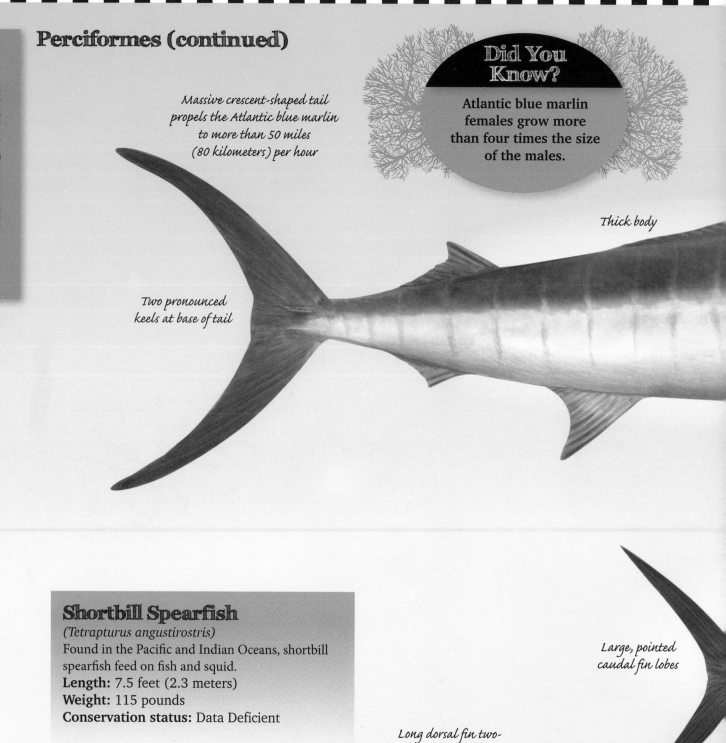

Massive crescent-shaped tail propels the Atlantic blue marlin to more than 50 miles (80 kilometers) per hour

Did You Know?

Atlantic blue marlin females grow more than four times the size of the males.

Thick body

Two pronounced keels at base of tail

Large, pointed caudal fin lobes

Shortbill Spearfish
(*Tetrapturus angustirostris*)
Found in the Pacific and Indian Oceans, shortbill spearfish feed on fish and squid.
Length: 7.5 feet (2.3 meters)
Weight: 115 pounds
Conservation status: Data Deficient

Long dorsal fin two-thirds body length

Long pelvic fins

Short bill slightly longer than lower jaw

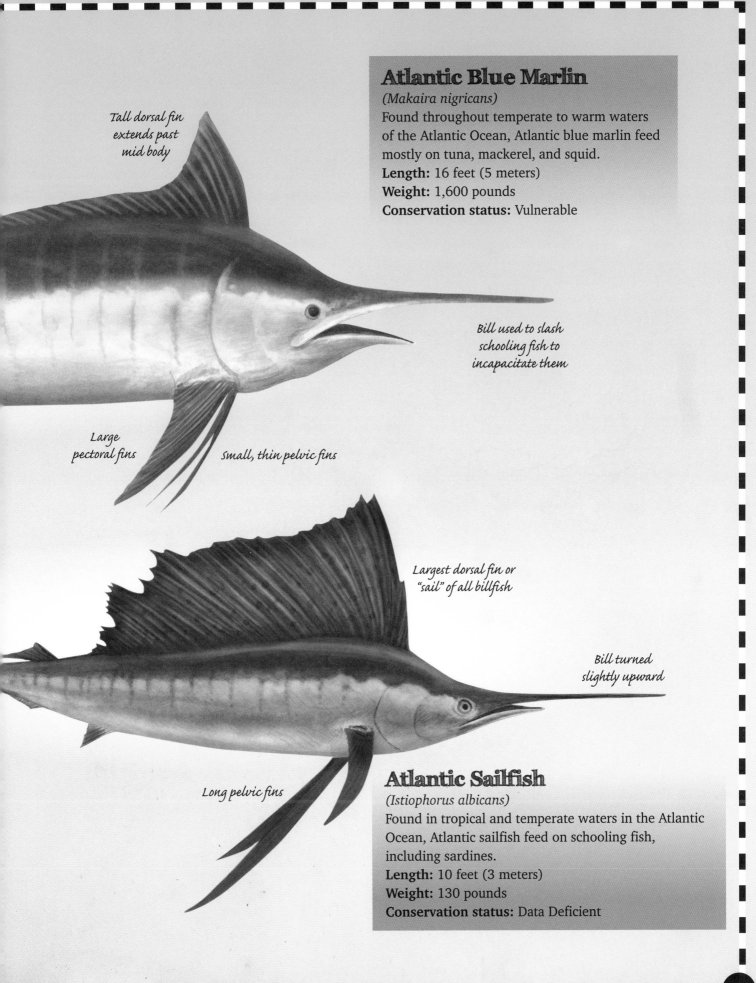

Tall dorsal fin extends past mid body

Atlantic Blue Marlin
(Makaira nigricans)
Found throughout temperate to warm waters of the Atlantic Ocean, Atlantic blue marlin feed mostly on tuna, mackerel, and squid.
Length: 16 feet (5 meters)
Weight: 1,600 pounds
Conservation status: Vulnerable

Bill used to slash schooling fish to incapacitate them

Large pectoral fins

Small, thin pelvic fins

Largest dorsal fin or "sail" of all billfish

Bill turned slightly upward

Atlantic Sailfish
(Istiophorus albicans)
Found in tropical and temperate waters in the Atlantic Ocean, Atlantic sailfish feed on schooling fish, including sardines.
Length: 10 feet (3 meters)
Weight: 130 pounds
Conservation status: Data Deficient

Long pelvic fins

Perciformes (continued)

Swordfish

(Xiphias gladius)
Found in open waters of the Atlantic, Indian, and Pacific Oceans, swordfish eat a variety of small- to medium-sized fish and crustaceans.
Length: 14 feet (4.3 meters)
Weight: 1,400 pounds
Conservation status: Least Concern

Very small second dorsal fin

Single caudal keel at base of tail

Large anal fin

Mahi-Mahi

(Coryphaena hippurus)
Found in tropical and subtropical oceans worldwide, mahi-mahi, also known as dolphinfish or dorado, feed on mackerel, flying fish, crabs, and squid.
Length: 4.6 feet (1.4 meters)
Weight: 40 pounds
Conservation status: Least Concern

Tall and long dorsal fin running length of body

Tall, thin caudal fins

Male or bull mahi-mahi (above) have a pronounced square head and are larger than the female (below)

Long pelvic fins

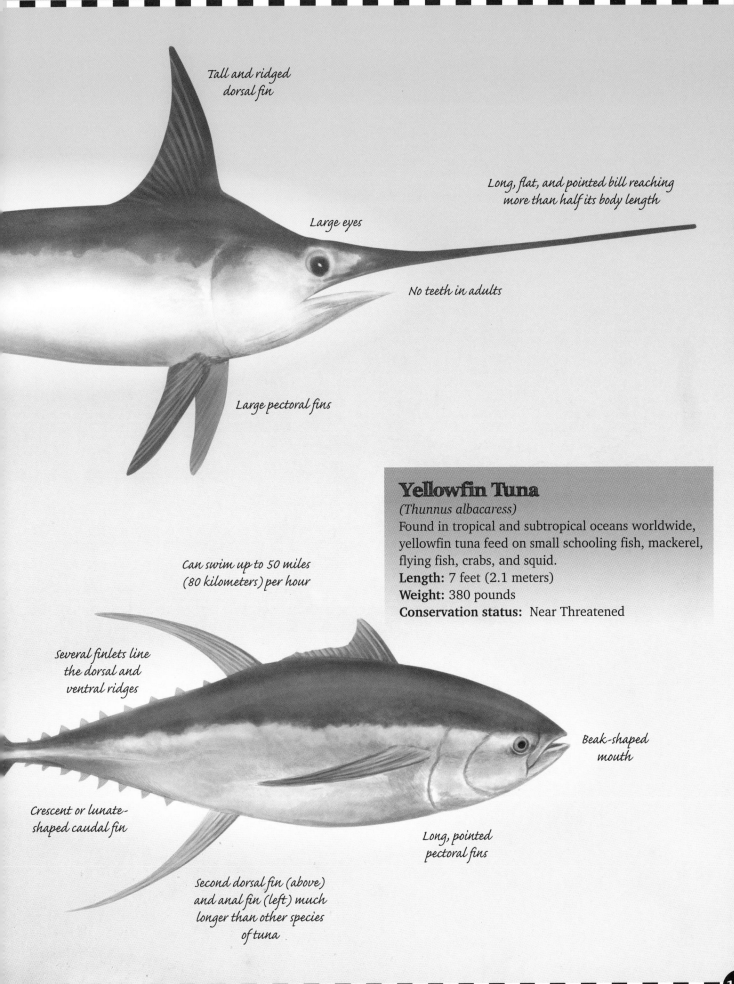

Tall and ridged
dorsal fin

Long, flat, and pointed bill reaching
more than half its body length

Large eyes

No teeth in adults

Large pectoral fins

Can swim up to 50 miles
(80 kilometers) per hour

Yellowfin Tuna
(Thunnus albacaress)
Found in tropical and subtropical oceans worldwide,
yellowfin tuna feed on small schooling fish, mackerel,
flying fish, crabs, and squid.
Length: 7 feet (2.1 meters)
Weight: 380 pounds
Conservation status: Near Threatened

Several finlets line
the dorsal and
ventral ridges

Beak-shaped
mouth

Crescent or lunate-
shaped caudal fin

Long, pointed
pectoral fins

Second dorsal fin (above)
and anal fin (left) much
longer than other species
of tuna

Fastest Fish in the Sea

Which fish do you think would win in a race: the yellowfin tuna, the sailfish, or the barracuda? Follow the lines to see who wins!

ANSWER ON PAGE 159

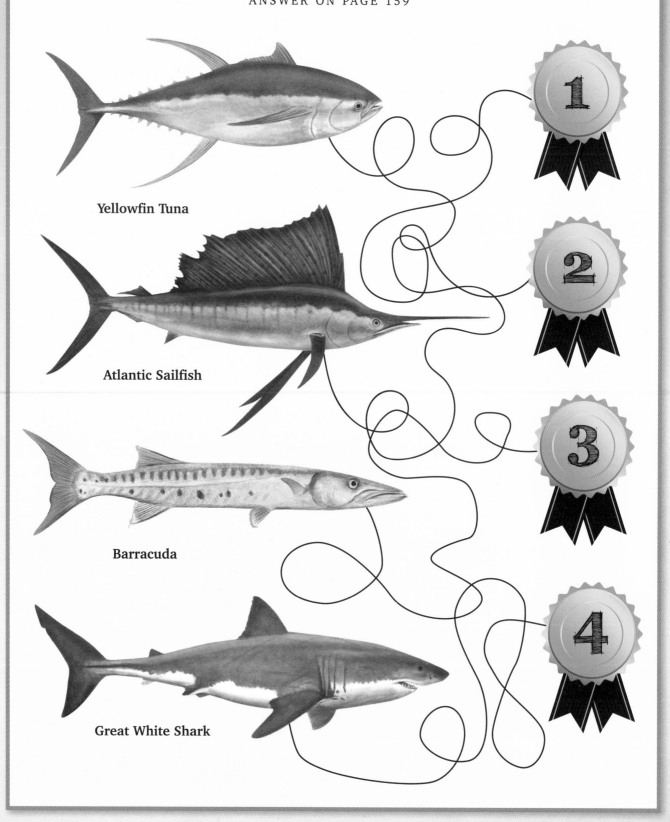

Yellowfin Tuna

Atlantic Sailfish

Barracuda

Great White Shark

Perciformes (continued)

Did You Know?

The clownfish's body is coated in a sugar-based mucus to prevent sea anemones from hunting it.

Common Clownfish
(Amphiprion ocellaris)

4.3 inches (11 centimeters)

Four Stripe Damselfish
(Dascyllus melanurus)

3.5 inches (9 centimeters)

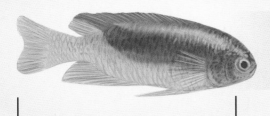

Yellow Belly Damselfish
(Pomacentrus auriventris)

2.8 inches (7 centimeters)

Sergeant Major
(Abudefduf saxatilis)

9 inches (23 centimeters)

Perciformes (continued)

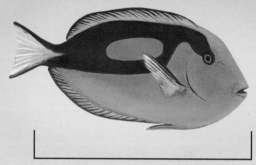

Blue Tang
(Paracanthurus hepatus)

12 inches (30 centimeters)

Whitemargin Unicornfish
(Naso annulatus)

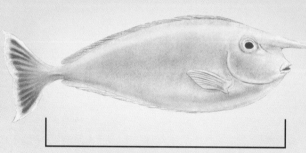

39 inches (100 centimeters)

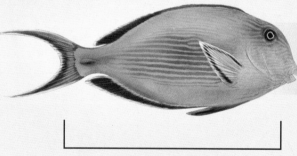

Sohal Tang
(Acanthurus sohal)

16 inches (41 centimeters)

Achilles Tang
(Acanthurus achilles)

10 inches (25 centimeters)

Moorish Idol
(Zanclus cornutus)

9 inches (23 centimeters)

Yellow Longnose Butterflyfish
(Forcipiger flavissimus)

8.5 inches (22 centimeters)

Did You Know?

Butterflyfish species tend to have an eyespot marking near the tail. Like on butterflies, this marking is believed to be a defense mechanism to protect from predators.

Copperband Butterflyfish
(Chelmon rostratus)

7.8 inches (20 centimeters)

Lined Butterflyfish
(Chaetodon lineolatus)

12 inches (30 centimeters)

Coral reefs are the most colorful scenes in the sea. Use colored pencils, markers, or crayons to add color below—and don't forget to add a few tropical fish!

Cephalopods

Cephalopods, meaning "head foot" in ancient Greek, get their name from their unique shape. A set of arms emerge directly from a large mantle, or head. With the exception of nautiluses, cephalopods are capable of changing color almost instantly. Some can even change their shape and skin texture to become virtually undetectable. This is possible because cephalopods don't have skeletons. Most cephalopods eject a cloud of ink to confuse predators. All cephalopods use a unique method of propulsion. They take in water through their mantle opening, and then expel it using a muscular contraction through an organ called a hyponome, or siphon. The quick release of water propels the cephalopod forward, much like a jet.

Order: Octopoda, Nautilida, Sepiida, Teuthida, and Vampyromorphida

Species: More than 800

Size Range: 0.39 inch (10 millimeters), bobtail squid, to 43 feet (13.1 meters), giant squid

Weight Range: 0.035 ounce, bobtail squid, to 1,650 pounds, colossal squid

Distribution: All oceans worldwide

Habitat: From shallow tropical waters to deep Arctic and Antarctic waters

Facts: Cephalopods are one of the oldest life-forms on Earth, having been around for 470 million years. Contrary to popular belief, octopuses do not have tentacles; they have arms. Squid, cuttlefish, and nautiluses have tentacles.

Cephalopoda Subclasses

Nautiloidea Subclass
- Nautilida order (Nautiluses)

Coleoidea Subclass
- Octopoda order (Octopuses)
- Teuthida order (Squid)
- Sepiida order (Cuttlefishes)
- Vampyromorphida order (Vampire Squid)

Place sticker here

Cephalopods, particularly octopuses and cuttlefish, are the smartest invertebrates on Earth!

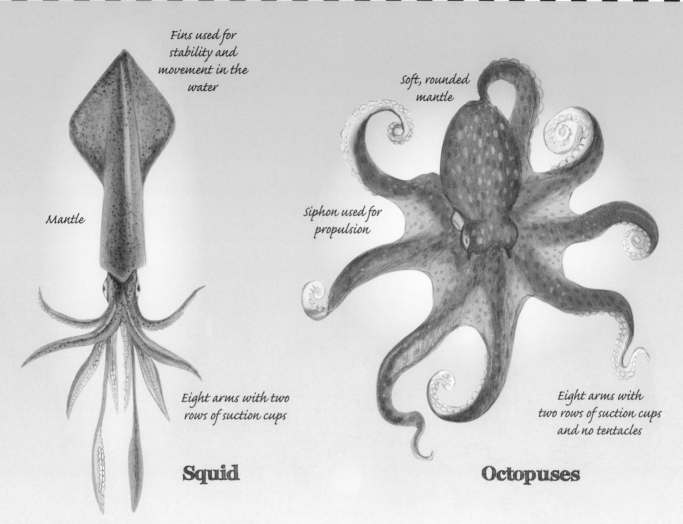

Fins used for stability and movement in the water

Mantle

Soft, rounded mantle

Siphon used for propulsion

Eight arms with two rows of suction cups

Eight arms with two rows of suction cups and no tentacles

Squid

Octopuses

Two feeding tentacles with clubs at the ends for catching prey

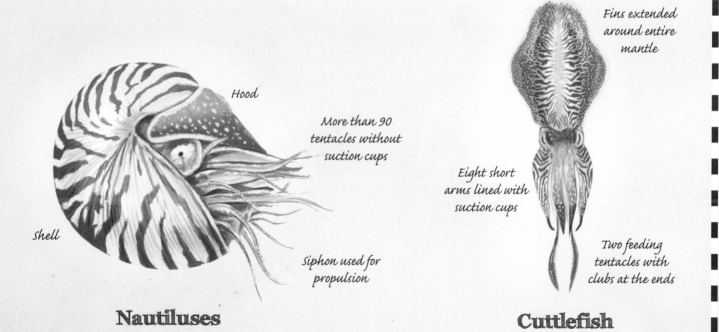

Hood

Fins extended around entire mantle

More than 90 tentacles without suction cups

Eight short arms lined with suction cups

Shell

Siphon used for propulsion

Two feeding tentacles with clubs at the ends

Nautiluses

Cuttlefish

Octopuses

The order Octopoda includes 300 octopus species. Octopuses are known for their rounded mantles, or heads, and their eight arms. Two rows of suction cups, called suckers, line the underside of the octopuses' arms. Octopuses perform delicate tasks with their arms, including opening shells and reaching into crevasses to find food. They use a hard beak located where the arms meet the mantle to crush their food. Octopuses are considered to be the most intelligent of all cephalopods.

Soft, rounded mantle

Greater Blue-Ringed Octopus
(Hapalochlaena lunulata)

Yellowish body with blue rings

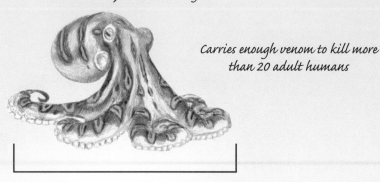

Carries enough venom to kill more than 20 adult humans

4 inches (10 centimeters), arm span,
2.8 ounces

White-Spotted Octopus
(Callistoctopus macropus)

Usually red-orange with white spots

5 feet (150 centimeters), arm span, 3 pounds

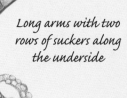

Long arms with two rows of suckers along the underside

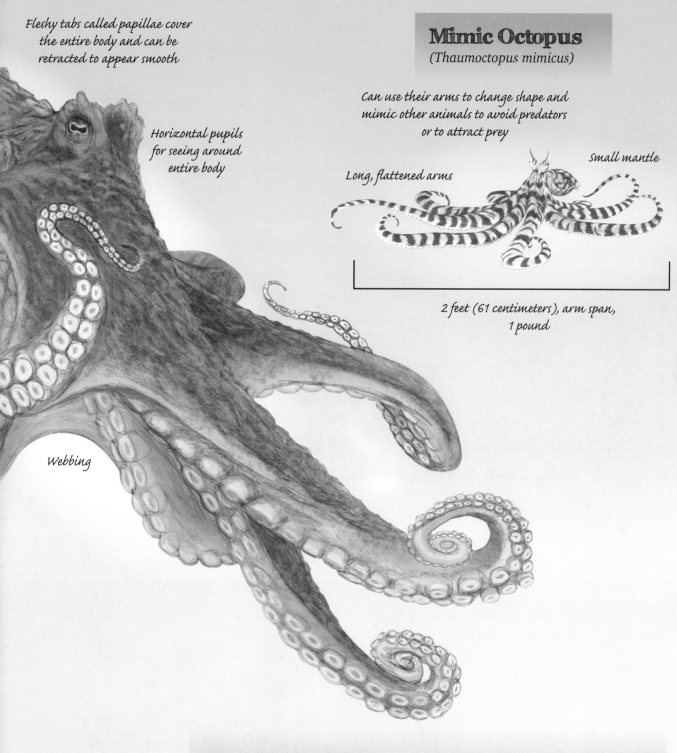

Fleshy tabs called papillae cover the entire body and can be retracted to appear smooth

Horizontal pupils for seeing around entire body

Webbing

Mimic Octopus
(Thaumoctopus mimicus)

Can use their arms to change shape and mimic other animals to avoid predators or to attract prey

Long, flattened arms

small mantle

2 feet (61 centimeters), arm span, 1 pound

Giant Pacific Octopus
(Enteroctopus dofleini)
Found in the cold waters around the North Pacific Ocean from Asia across the Bering Strait through California, giant Pacific octopuses prey on shrimp, crabs, scallops, clams, lobsters, and fish.
Length: 16 feet (5 meters), arm span
Weight: 110 pounds
Conservation status: Not Assessed

Octopus Color-By-Number

Bring this octopus to life with markers, colored pencils, or crayons!
To figure out which shade to use in each section of the picture, match the number
in the space to the corresponding bubble below.

ANSWER ON PAGE 159

Cephalopod Word Search

Cephalopods are some of the most fascinating animals in the sea!
As you learn about cool tentacled (or armed) creatures, get to
know some of the words associated with them.
Can you spot all the words below?

ANSWERS ON PAGE 159

- ☐ Beak
- ☐ Chromatophores
- ☐ Cuttlebone
- ☐ Hood
- ☐ Mantle
- ☐ Radula
- ☐ Siphon
- ☐ Suckers
- ☐ Tentacle
- ☐ Webbing

```
C G S U H A Q U C J Z W Z I B A Z A Q S
V W U R E L K M A U G U G D S Z D O F I
P D C M A P W X C E T H P M H F Y V B P
A X K H V H G X S Y I T E H V O W L N H
K Q E S I B K L B Q Q S L G W U O W J O
D Y R I C C E J X N C W T E E J Z D J N
O T S O X V P A N V R G G E B N M P X T
F M E A J A G L K T J F M M B O W I F L
C I Q B X D S W K M G B I L I F N W S W
V O B D J X R J O D L Q B V N H H E W R
U G C H Q I D Y H T U U U T G K M B W M
C H R O M A T O P H O R E S A W Y I O A
V H G V L A W H G O W S J Y E S X M T R
O G I M Y H J A N T D A A K P M R G I N
N Q Q V N N L M T V W J V D N E D K I S
J K C L F L C M G J T E N T A C L E U Y
M A N T L E Y X U M Q D Q R O I Q E J P
Q G B W D S Q W X D I T F P S W Z H M C
G Y C N L G X S H W W Q K V T H K B U P
T K B U E T R A D U L A L G N S E Y I V
```

Squid

The Teuthida order is comprised of more than 300 species of squid. Squid have a distinct, large mantle with two fins at the end, as well as eight arms and two longer feeding tentacles. Unique to squid and cuttlefish, the feeding tentacles are usually kept retracted between the arms when not hunting. All Teuthida have skin covered in small cells called "chromatophores." These cells let the squid change color instantly to avoid predators or to communicate. The Teuthida order includes the largest of all cephalopods, the giant squid, which can reach 43 feet (13.1 meters) in length, and the colossal squid, which can weigh as much as 1,650 pounds (748.4 kilograms).

Large mantle

swimming fins

Hard beak at the center of the arms made of a hard material called chitin, not bone. Small, spiny tongue called a radula pulls prey into mouth.

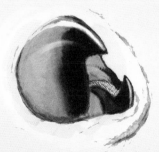

Feeding tentacle club is surrounded by muscle

A ring of hard and sharp serrated edges of the feeding tentacle suction cup help secure prey

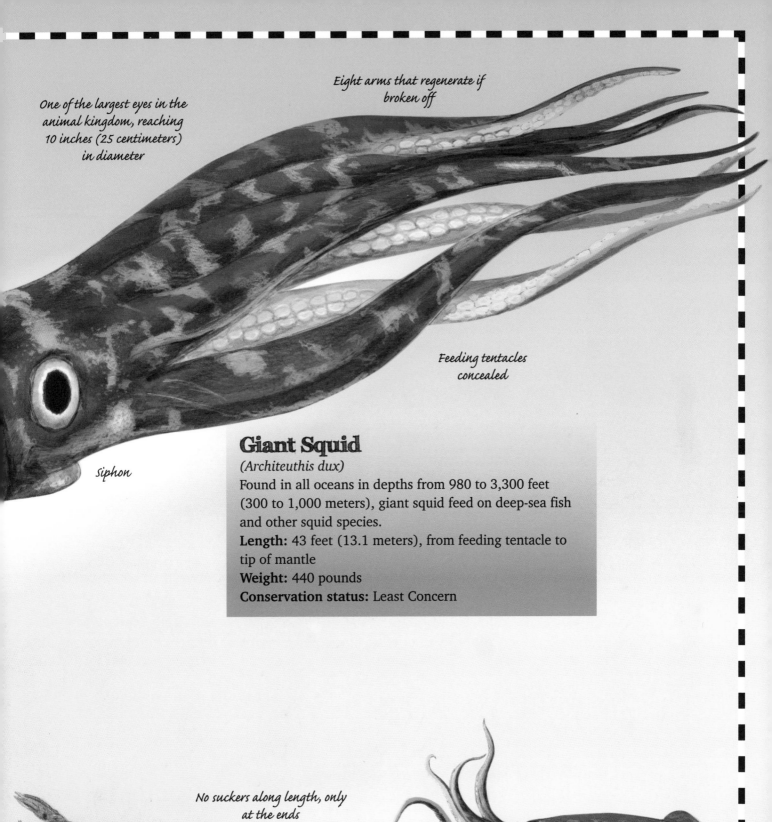

One of the largest eyes in the animal kingdom, reaching 10 inches (25 centimeters) in diameter

Eight arms that regenerate if broken off

Feeding tentacles concealed

Siphon

Giant Squid
(Architeuthis dux)
Found in all oceans in depths from 980 to 3,300 feet (300 to 1,000 meters), giant squid feed on deep-sea fish and other squid species.
Length: 43 feet (13.1 meters), from feeding tentacle to tip of mantle
Weight: 440 pounds
Conservation status: Least Concern

No suckers along length, only at the ends

Feeding tentacles longer than the overall length of arms and mantle

Squid (continued)

Colossal Squid

(Mesonychoteuthis hamiltoni)
Found throughout the southern oceans surrounding Antarctica,
colossal squid feed on fish, as well as other squid species.
Length: 42 feet (12.8 meters), from feeding tentacle to tip of mantle
Weight: 1,650 pounds
Conservation status: Least Concern

*Short arms with two
feeding tentacles
tucked inside*

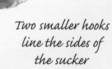

Siphon

*Feeding tentacle clubs lined with sharp,
swiveling hooks designed to latch onto prey*

*Rotating hooks can
reach up to 1.5 inches
(3.8 centimeters)*

*Two smaller hooks
line the sides of
the sucker*

Sizable Squid

Just how large are these monsters of
the sea? Mark the object that best
represents the size of the giant squid.
ANSWER ON PAGE 159

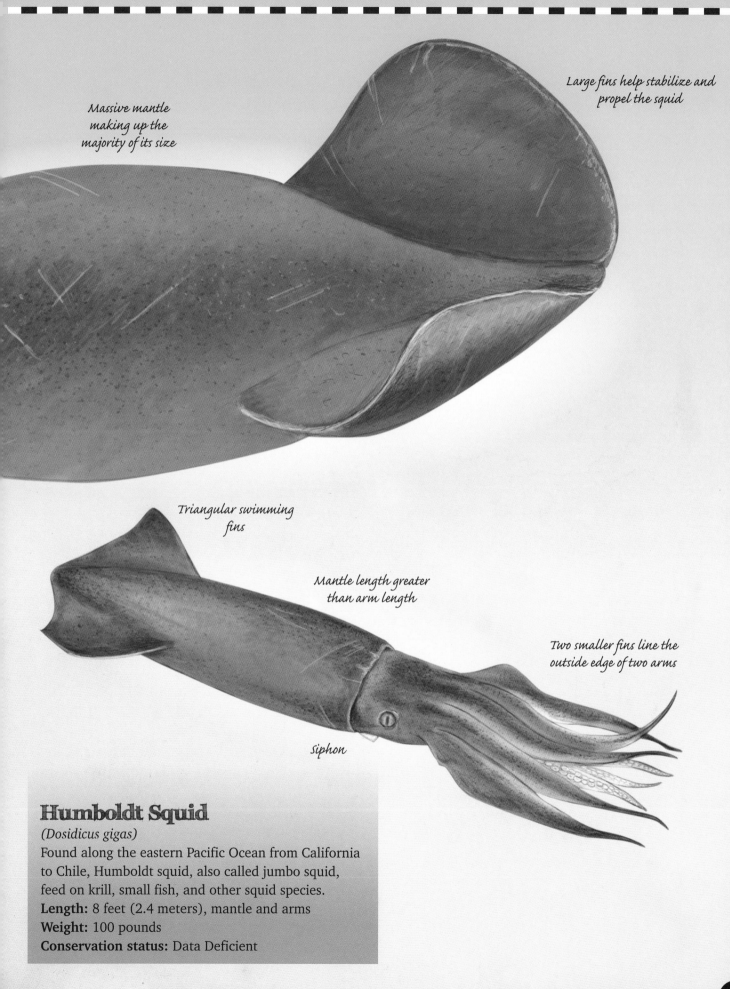

Large fins help stabilize and propel the squid

Massive mantle making up the majority of its size

Triangular swimming fins

Mantle length greater than arm length

Two smaller fins line the outside edge of two arms

Siphon

Humboldt Squid

(Dosidicus gigas)

Found along the eastern Pacific Ocean from California to Chile, Humboldt squid, also called jumbo squid, feed on krill, small fish, and other squid species.

Length: 8 feet (2.4 meters), mantle and arms
Weight: 100 pounds
Conservation status: Data Deficient

Cuttlefish

Long fin undulates to propel in any direction

siphon

The 120 species of the Sepiida order, called cuttlefish, are unique because they have an internal shell called a cuttlebone. Like their squid relatives, they have two long feeding tentacles, skin that can change color, and a siphon that propels them forward.

Common Cuttlefish

(Sepia officinalis)
Found in the Mediterranean, North, and Baltic Seas, common cuttlefish feed on a variety of prey including crustaceans, fish, small octopuses, and squid.
Length: 19.2 inches (49 centimeters), mantle length
Weight: 8 pounds
Conservation status: Least Concern

Did You Know?

The cuttlefish has a W-shaped pupil!

Vampire Squid

The Vampyromorphida order is represented by only one known species: the vampire squid. A deep-sea species, the vampire squid shares many traits with both octopuses and squid. They have long sensory organs called velar filaments that are used to capture dead plankton and other organic matter floating in the water.

Arms lined with fleshy, spine-like projections called cirri

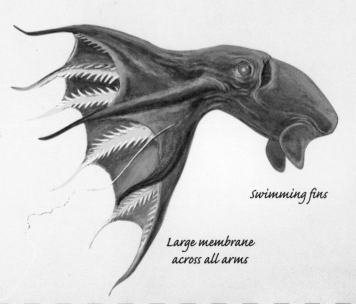

swimming fins

Large membrane across all arms

Vampire Squid

(Vampyroteuthis infernalis)
Found throughout temperate and tropical oceans in depths from 2,000 to 3,000 feet (600 to 900 meters), vampire squid feed on organic debris in the water.
Length: 1 foot (30 centimeters)
Weight: Not available
Conservation status: Data Deficient

What Am I?

Test your detective instincts as you figure out each animal below.
Find and place the matching stickers!

ANSWERS ON PAGE 159

Animal 1

I have eight arms with two rows of suction cups. My mantle is soft and round, and my pupils are horizontal. I am considered to be very clever! What am I?

Place sticker here

Animal 2

I have a very distinct orange, black, and white coloring. To protect me from sea anemones, I am coated in a sugary mucus. What am I?

Place sticker here

Animal 3

I have a long, ribbon-like body without any pectoral or caudal fins. I have sharp, curved teeth and two jaws—one is hidden in my throat! What am I?

Place sticker here

Animal 4

I have a very wide, U-shaped head with a small eye on each end. I have a large dorsal fin but a small mouth designed for bottom feeding. What am I?

Place sticker here

Nautiluses

The Nautilida order contains the most primitive of all cephalopods. It is the only remaining order to still have an outer shell. There are only six species in the order. Nautilida have basic eyes called pinhole eyes that lack a lens—most other animals in nature have lenses. Because of this, a limited amount of light comes into the receptors, which gives them poor eyesight in darker conditions.

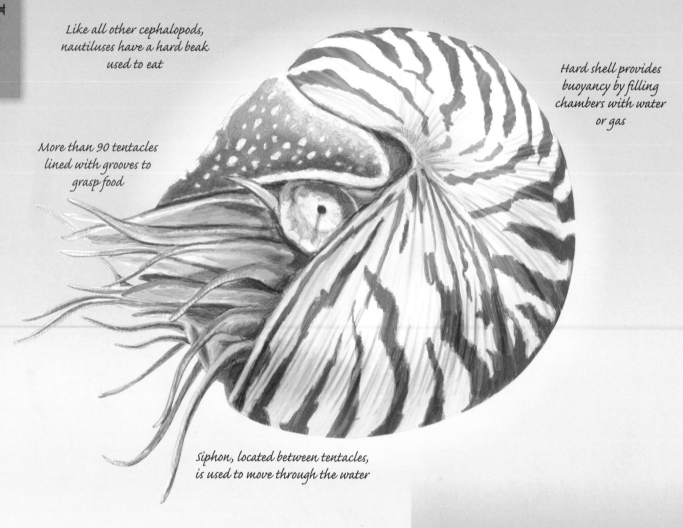

Like all other cephalopods, nautiluses have a hard beak used to eat

Hard shell provides buoyancy by filling chambers with water or gas

More than 90 tentacles lined with grooves to grasp food

Siphon, located between tentacles, is used to move through the water

Did You Know?

If threatened, the nautilus can retract inside its shell by closing its hood.

Chambered Nautilus

(Nautilus pompilius)
Found in the South Pacific Ocean near reefs, chambered nautiluses mostly scavenge dead sea creatures, but are known to eat live shellfish and crabs.
Length: 8 inches (20 centimeters), shell diameter
Weight: 1.8 pounds
Conservation status: Data Deficient

A Silly Sea Story

Create a random list of words using the prompts below. Then fill in the corresponding words to complete your story. Remember that a noun is a person, place, or thing. An adjective is a descriptive word, and a verb is an action. Try not to laugh!

Plural Noun:_____   Plural Noun:_____

Adjective:_____   Noun:_____

Adjective:_____   Adjective:_____

Adjective:_____   Adjective:_____

Plural Noun:_____   Plural Noun:_____

Plural Noun:_____   Adjective:_____

Verb: _____   Adjective:_____

In the ocean, there are many interesting sea _____.
                                                    Plural Noun

Some are _____ and some are _____, but all have one
              Adjective   *Adjective*

thing in common: They're all _____. To see ocean _____
                                Adjective   *Plural Noun*

up close, you can visit tide pools or swim in coral _____.
                                                        Plural Noun

But don't touch anything—they might _____!
                                            Verb

One of the most exciting marine _____ to see is the
                                        Plural Noun

tropical _____. You'll know you've seen one if it looks
              Noun

_____ and acts _____. Even if you don't find any
    Adjective   *Adjective*

sea _____, you can still be _____ knowing that you had
        Plural Noun   *Adjective*

a(n) _____ time outdoors.
            Adjective

Marine Birds

Marine birds are unlike other aquatic birds because they have developed special adaptations for life in and around salt water. Though they get the majority of their drinking water from the prey they eat, most marine birds can drink salt water. Like many birds, most marine birds have a gland at the base of their tail that secretes a waxy oil. They use their beaks to spread this oil over their feathers to waterproof them. Some species, like penguins, have adapted to become master swimmers and have lost their ability to fly.

Order: *Charadriiformes, Pelecaniformes, Phaethontiformes, Procellariiformes, Sphenisciformes, and Suliformes*

Species: *More than 600*

Size Range: *11-inch wingspan (28 centimeters), storm petrel, to 11.6 feet (3.5 meters), wandering albatross*

Weight Range: *0.1 ounce (3 grams), storm petrel, to 99 pounds (45 kilograms), emperor penguin*

Distribution: *All oceans worldwide*

Habitat: *From warm, tropical waters to cold Arctic and Antarctic waters*

Facts: *In general, marine birds grow slower than their land-based counterparts. Collectively, marine birds are distributed throughout the globe from the Arctic Circle to Antarctica.*

Marine Bird Orders

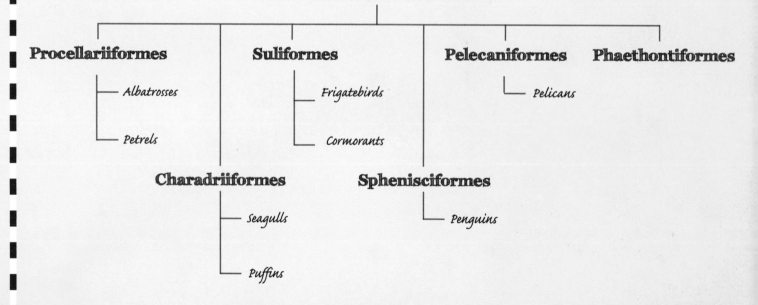

Procellariiformes
- Albatrosses
- Petrels

Suliformes
- Frigatebirds
- Cormorants

Pelecaniformes
- Pelicans

Phaethontiformes

Charadriiformes
- Seagulls
- Puffins

Sphenisciformes
- Penguins

Albatrosses & Petrels

The Procellariiformes order consists of four families and 125 species of marine birds. They are excellent fliers. Some can travel up to 10,000 miles without ever setting foot on dry land. They are highly social and form colonies of thousands of birds during breeding time. As adults, many species will return to the same spot where they hatched.

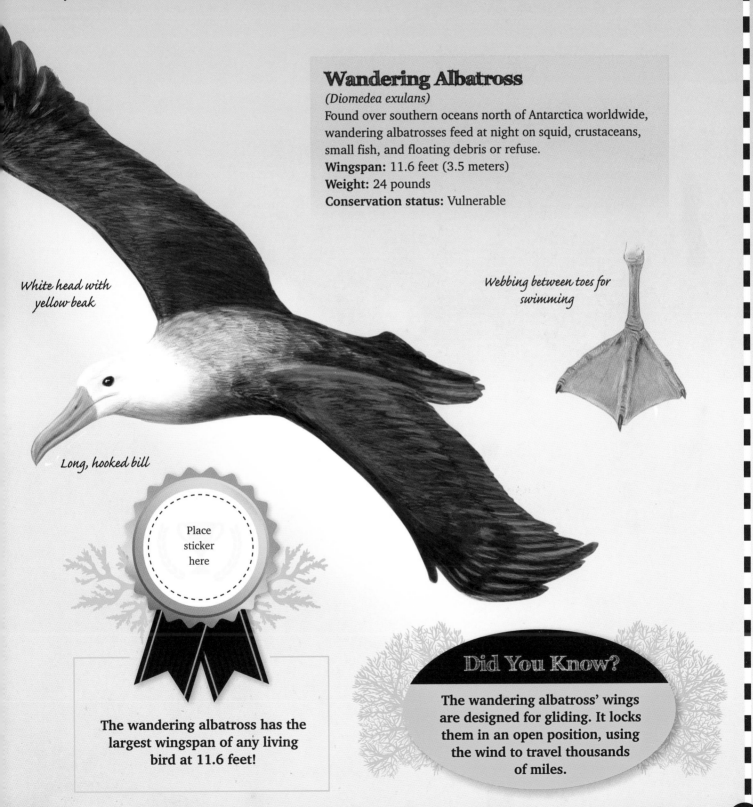

Wandering Albatross

(Diomedea exulans)
Found over southern oceans north of Antarctica worldwide, wandering albatrosses feed at night on squid, crustaceans, small fish, and floating debris or refuse.
Wingspan: 11.6 feet (3.5 meters)
Weight: 24 pounds
Conservation status: Vulnerable

White head with yellow beak

Webbing between toes for swimming

Long, hooked bill

Place sticker here

The wandering albatross has the largest wingspan of any living bird at 11.6 feet!

Did You Know?

The wandering albatross' wings are designed for gliding. It locks them in an open position, using the wind to travel thousands of miles.

Seagulls & Puffins

There are about 350 species in the Charadriiformes order, including some recognizable shorebirds such as seagulls and sandpipers, as well as more unique species like the puffin. Charadriiformes are distributed worldwide on all continents. The majority of Charadriiformes are strong fliers and inhabit coasts, shallow waterways, and marshes, where they scavenge or hunt for small fish and insects.

Ring-Billed Gull
(Larus delawarensis)

49-inch (124-centimeter) wingspan

Gray feathers on top with white feathers underneath

Black stripe on tip of bill

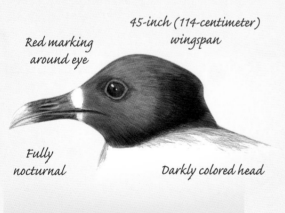

45-inch (114-centimeter) wingspan

Red marking around eye

Fully nocturnal

Darkly colored head

Swallow-Tailed Gull
(Creagrus furcatus)

25-inch (63-centimeter) wingspan

Brightly colored bill during mating season. Later coloring changes to gray

Atlantic Puffin
(Fratercula arctica)

Pelicans

Pelecaniformes are large marine birds with long beaks and throat sacs (or gular pouches) under their lower jaws. They hunt small fish and squid using various methods, including diving from the air into the water and foraging from shorelines or the surface of the water for food. They have four webbed toes on their feet, whereas the majority of marine birds only have three.

Brown Pelican

(Pelecanus occidentalis)
Found throughout the Gulf, Atlantic, and Pacific coasts in the Americas, brown pelicans feed almost exclusively on small fish.
Wingspan: 7.5 feet (2.3 meters)
Weight: 11 pounds
Conservation status: Least Concern

Long, pronounced bill with hook at tip to help catch fish

Forward-facing eyes

Four webbed toes on each foot

Pelicans fold their necks under their heads while resting or flying

During mating season, American white pelicans grow a flattened horn; after mating season, the horn falls off

American White Pelican

(Pelecanus erythrorhynchos)

10-foot (3-meter) wingspan

141

Frigatebirds & Cormorants

The order of Suliformes can be broken down into four families: Fregatidae (frigatebirds), Sulidae (gannets and boobies), Phalacrocoracidae (cormorants), and Anhingidae (anhingas and darters). Each is an active predator with the exception of the magnificent frigatebird.

Magnificent Frigatebird

(Fregata magnificens)

Found across tropical and subtropical waters off the Americas, from northern Mexico to Ecuador on the Pacific coast and from Florida to Brazil along the Atlantic coast, magnificent frigatebirds feed on fish from the surface of the ocean but are also known to steal other birds' catches.

Wingspan: 8 feet (2.4 meters)

Weight: 4 pounds

Conservation status: Least Concern

Long, angular wings

Mostly dark, black feathers

Forked tail

Frigatebirds often harass other marine birds to steal their prey

Male frigatebirds inflate their throat pouches during mating season to attract mates

Where in the World?

Write the name of the correct bird in the map key: **Flightless cormorant, Great cormorant, or Magnificent frigatebird**

⬤ _____

⬤ _____

⬤ _____

ANSWERS ON PAGE 159

Great Cormorant
(Phalacrocorax carbo)
Found in coastal waters from the Americas to Europe, Scandinavia, Asia, and Southern Africa, great cormorants dive for small fish, snakes, and eels.
Wingspan: 5 feet (1.5 meters)
Weight: 12 pounds
Conservation status: Least Concern

Hooked bill

Broad wings

Long, narrow bill with hooked tip

Smaller wings more suited for swimming than flying

Cormorants spread their wings to dry after emerging from the water

Four-toed webbed feet

Flightless Cormorant
(Phalacrocorax harrisi)
Found only in the Galapagos Islands, flightless cormorants feed on small fish, octopuses, and squid.
Length: 39 inches (1 meter)
Weight: 12 pounds
Conservation status: Vulnerable

Penguins

The most iconic of all the marine birds are the Sphenisciformes, or penguins. Their bodies are uniquely shaped for swimming, and their black backs and white undersides make them difficult to be seen from above or below when in the water. This helps keep both their prey and predators from distinguishing them from their surroundings. Sphenisciformes spend an equal amount of time in the ocean and on land, and live exclusively in the Southern Hemisphere (except for the Galapagos penguin, which lives around the equator).

Penguin Match-up

Can you identify each penguin species?
Match the images to their descriptions by writing the correct letters in the boxes below!

ANSWERS ON PAGE 159

Chinstrap Penguin

(Pygoscelis antarcticus)
Description: Thin black marking around neck, white underside.
Size: 28 inches (71 centimeters), 11 pounds
Diet: Fish, but also squid and krill
Location: On coastlines along sub-Antarctic islands surrounding Antarctica
Conservation status: Least Concern

Gentoo Penguin

(Pygoscelis papua)
Description: White spot around eyes, wings used to propel the penguin forward under water, webbed feet used as rudders.
Size: 35 inches (90 centimeters), 20 pounds
Diet: Fish, krill, and squid
Location: On coastlines along Antarctica as well as the sub-Antarctic islands
Conservation status: Least Concern

A

B

☐ Emperor Penguin

(Aptenodytes forsteri)

Description: Large, bulky body. Pale yellow breast. Long, flipper-like wings.

Size: 4 feet (1.2 meters), 100 pounds

Diet: Fish, but also squid and krill

Location: On coastlines throughout Antarctica

Conservation status: Near Threatened

F

☐ Galapagos Penguin

(Spheniscus mendiculus)

Description: White ring marking from eye to eye around neck, small body with broad wings, and short tail.

Size: 19 inches (48 centimeters), 5.5 pounds

Diet: Small fish

Location: In the Galapagos Islands off the coast of Ecuador

Conservation status: Endangered

Did You Know?

Penguins move as efficiently in the water as other birds move in the air.

☐ Northern Rockhopper Penguin

(Eudyptes moseleyi)

Description: Unique yellow-feathered crest, red bill and eyes, strong legs.

Size: 20 inches (51 centimeters), 6.6 pounds

Diet: Fish, squid, and krill

Location: On coastlines along sub-Antarctic islands in the South Atlantic and Pacific Oceans

Conservation status: Endangered

☐ King Penguin

(Aptenodytes patagonicus)

Description: Relatively long beak, gray to black back, white underside, and webbing between three toes.

Size: 3.25 feet (0.99 meters), 40 pounds

Diet: Fish, squid, and krill

Location: On coastlines along sub-Antarctic islands as far north as the southern tip of South America

Conservation status: Least Concern

C

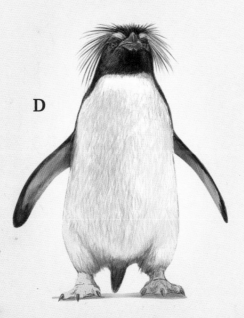

D

E

Marine Reptiles

For millions of years, marine reptiles dominated the oceans. Their reign ended about 65 million years ago with the dinosaurs. Now, of the roughly 12,000 species of reptiles on Earth, fewer than 100 marine reptile species remain—all of which closely resemble their land-based counterparts. Most still have to go ashore to lay eggs or rest. All reptiles are cold-blooded, meaning that they cannot regulate their own body temperature. Instead, they rely on an external source, such as the sun, to warm their bodies. The remaining marine reptile species include one crocodile, seven sea turtles, one iguana, and about 62 sea snakes. Each have adapted to, and flourish in, marine environments.

Order: Squamata, Crocodilia, and Testudines

Species: Approximately 100

Size Range: 10 inches (25 centimeters), marine iguana, to 18 feet (5.5 meters), saltwater crocodile

Weight Range: 1.7 pounds (0.8 kilogram), blue-banded sea snake, to 2,000 pounds (907 kilograms), saltwater crocodile

Distribution: All oceans worldwide

Habitat: From warm, coastal tropical waters to open ocean

Facts: Marine reptiles dominated the oceans in prehistoric times. They now only make up one-tenth of all reptile species. The largest of all living reptiles is the saltwater crocodile. The marine iguana is the only known lizard to have adapted to life in marine environments.

Marine Reptile Orders

Squamata	Crocodilia	Testudines
Marine iguana	Saltwater crocodiles	Sea turtles
Sea snakes		

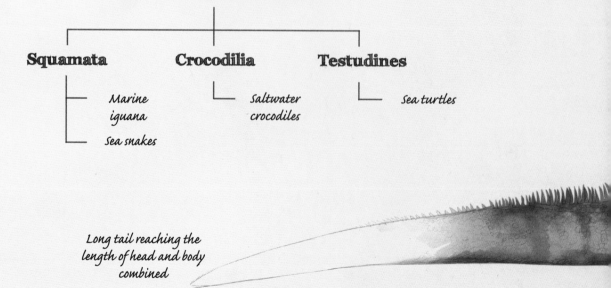

Long tail reaching the length of head and body combined

Lizards & Snakes

The Squamata order is by far the largest order of reptiles, consisting of more than 10,000 species. This is the second-most abundant order of vertebrates after Perciformes (bony fish). Squamata represents all scaled reptiles, which include snakes and lizards. There are 63 marine Squamata species combined. All have adaptations for life in the ocean, including specialized glands to expel salt from the salt water they absorb or drink, and tall, flattened tails to help with swimming.

Spines running from head along back and tail

Tail is moved side to side underwater

Thick, hard lips to help scrape algae from rocks in the ocean

Legs tucked close to body when swimming

Thick, powerful neck

Marine Iguana
(Amblyrhynchus cristatus)
Found only on the shorelines of the Galapagos Islands off the coast of Ecuador, marine iguanas (also known as Galapagos marine iguanas) feed almost exclusively on underwater marine algae.
Length: 19 inches (48 centimeters), head and body
Weight: 26 pounds
Conservation status: Vulnerable

Long claws help anchor the marine iguana to rocks when feeding under water

Lizards & Snakes (continued)

Yellow-Bellied Sea Snake

(Hydrophis platura)

Found throughout the tropical Indo-Pacific region, as well as along the Pacific coast from northern Mexico to Peru, yellow-bellied sea snakes feed exclusively on fish. They require fresh water for drinking, which they get from rainfall on the surface of the ocean.

Length: 35 inches (89 centimeters)

Weight: 1.2 pounds

Conservation status: Least Concern

Did You Know?

All sea snakes paralyze their prey with a powerful toxin injected through fangs. They also have a gland under the tongue that eliminates salt.

Long head with valved nostrils to keep water out

Flattened tail acts as a paddle under water

Brightly colored yellow and black pattern

Covered in non-overlapping scales

Banded Sea Krait

(Laticauda colubrina)

Found widespread in the Indian and western Pacific Oceans, banded sea krait, also called the yellow-lipped sea krait, feed on a variety of eel species and small fish.

Length: 56 inches (1.4 meters)

Weight: 3 pounds

Conservation status: Least Concern

Broad, rounded head

Flattened tail

Long, cylindrical body

Slithering Sea Snake

Find the route that leads the sea snake to shore!

ANSWER ON PAGE 159

A

B

C

D

E

End

Saltwater Crocodile

Crocodilians are large, semi-aquatic, predatory reptiles represented by 23 species, most of which live near shorelines around fresh or brackish water. They include three families: Alligatoridae (alligators and caimans), Crocodylidae (crocodiles), and Gavialidae (gharials). There is only one marine species: the saltwater crocodile. Saltwater crocodiles are the largest of all living reptiles, reaching close to 20 feet (6 meters) in length. They are considered an aggressive species and dominate their environments as apex predators.

Did You Know?

A valve in the mouth keeps water from entering the crocodile's airways when submerged.

Ear valves prevent water from entering

64 to 68 conical teeth used for grasping

Top of body covered in scaly protrusions called "scutes"

Long, powerful tail used for propulsion under water

Webbed feet

Saltwater Crocodile

(Crocodylus porosus)
Found in coastal areas from India through southern Asia and northern Australia, saltwater crocodiles feed on a wide array of prey, including fish, birds, deer, boar, and sea turtles.
Length: 20 feet (6 meters), head and tail
Weight: 2,200 pounds
Conservation status: Least Concern

Place sticker here

The saltwater crocodile has the strongest bite of any animal in this book! Its bite force is 3,700 pounds per square inch. Ouch!

Draw a Saltwater Crocodile!

Use the blank grid to draw what you see in each square of the croc portrait on the right. Start with a sketch, and then give it bumpy, cracked reptilian skin with markers, colored pencils, or crayons!

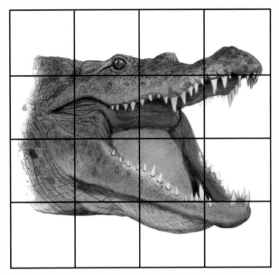

Sea Turtles

Testudines is the reptilian order composed of turtles, terrapins, and tortoises. There are more than 300 species, and all are known for their characteristic shell covering their backs. Their shells are used mainly as protection from predators. There are seven species of sea turtles, also called marine turtles, that spend the vast majority of their lives in the ocean. The females only go onto dry land to lay eggs. All seven species are considered either endangered, critically endangered, or vulnerable, and they are protected worldwide.

Hawksbill Sea Turtle

(*Eretmochelys imbricata*)
Found in all tropical waters of Indian, Pacific, and Atlantic Oceans, hawksbill sea turtles feed on sea sponges, crustaceans, fish, and algae.
Length: 3 feet (0.9 meter)
Weight: 190 pounds
Conservation status: Critically Endangered

Beak forms a point

Overlapping scales, or scutes, on shell

Did You Know?

Leatherback sea turtles are the only sea turtles to have a soft shell.

Five dorsal ridges on back

Leatherback Sea Turtle

(*Dermochelys coriacea*)
Found in all oceans worldwide, leatherback turtles, sometimes called leathery turtles, feed only on jellyfish.
Length: 8 feet (2.4 meters)
Weight: 1,600 pounds
Conservation status: Vulnerable

Massive front flippers reaching as long as body length

Shell covered in large scales called "scutes"

Loggerhead Sea Turtle

(Caretta caretta)

Found in all tropical waters of the Indian, Atlantic, and Pacific Oceans, and the Mediterranean Sea, loggerhead sea turtles have a varied diet, including invertebrates, starfish, sponges, jellyfish, and squid.

Length: 3 feet (0.9 meter)
Weight: 250 pounds
Conservation status: Vulnerable

Large head for body size

Two small claws on front edge of front flippers

Beak with no teeth

Hind flippers smaller than foreflippers

Flippers used for swimming

Triangular hind flippers

Green Sea Turtle

(Chelonia mydas)

Found in all tropical and subtropical oceans worldwide, green sea turtles start life as carnivores eating mollusks, jellyfish, and crustaceans. Adults later become herbivores, feeding on seagrass and algae.

Length: 5 feet (1.5 meters)
Weight: 420 pounds
Conservation status: Endangered

Use markers, colored pencils, or crayons to color these soaring sea turtles!

Aqua Awards

Fill in the blanks to award
your favorite marine animals!
Remember: There are no
wrong answers.

My all-time favorite
marine animal:

_____

_____

The scariest creature
in the sea:

_____

_____

The most fascinating
creature in the sea:

_____

_____

The most beautiful
creature in the sea:

_____

_____

The strangest-looking
creature in the sea:

_____

_____

The marine animals
I've seen in person:

_____

_____

_____

_____

_____

The marine animals I
hope to see someday:

_____

_____

_____

_____

_____

Answer Key

Page 9:

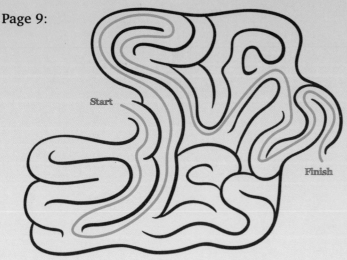

Start

Finish

Page 13

thick, waterproof, and white

Page 17

```
Z  F  L  I  P  P  E  R  S  Q  M  E  B  S  E  E  Q  S  L  M
A  I  O  O  T  F  B  B  E  H  S  R  G  O  C  N  S  R  G  H
K  D  I  R  C  Y  S  R  S  K  F  I  I  Z  H  S  Z  Y  L  B
G  C  A  Z  A  J  T  A  S  V  M  R  W  F  O  H  C  A  Q  U
K  H  K  D  L  G  M  D  R  Q  C  H  E  K  L  Z  T  S  L  F
M  Q  I  K  L  F  E  Y  G  Q  W  W  M  B  O  J  B  H  Y  R
Z  M  N  M  O  E  C  C  Z  H  V  V  H  T  C  A  D  Q  C  P
Y  U  F  X  L  U  M  A  C  M  V  W  U  T  A  B  F  P  N  Z
H  W  J  C  O  E  L  R  J  L  L  M  Y  A  T  O  L  J  W  G
M  E  S  H  K  Z  F  D  Z  Q  C  J  L  E  I  C  E  D  B  L
G  M  A  A  S  X  N  I  X  M  F  P  X  D  O  I  M  W  L  Q
Z  E  O  X  J  D  M  A  D  W  E  L  G  E  N  M  W  K  O  Q
F  U  A  P  I  P  X  B  G  Y  S  S  O  Z  A  E  Q  E  W  K
B  L  C  I  Z  I  F  D  D  Z  Z  T  J  Z  A  L  E  S  H  O
A  T  U  Q  W  J  M  V  Z  V  A  I  R  U  L  O  W  Z  O  P
L  O  K  K  B  L  U  B  B  E  R  K  A  V  B  N  F  M  L  D
E  Z  I  K  E  L  V  E  D  O  P  M  C  A  L  F  X  J  E  D
E  Y  F  U  H  G  G  M  G  C  X  Z  G  Y  G  Q  V  U  T  U
N  L  J  D  F  S  D  P  D  T  N  F  J  X  W  W  C  V  I  T
S  V  V  S  D  J  W  J  W  L  P  F  C  E  P  X  X  W  B  K
```

Page 19

A: Harbor seal
B: Hooded seal
C: Ribbon seal

Page 20

Killer whale

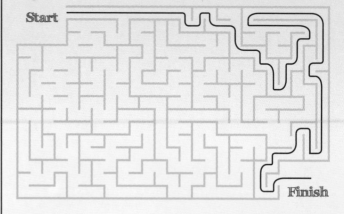

Page 22

The elephant seal nose can make very loud sounds.

Page 24

☐ True seals can smell and see well on land.
☐ True seals can only smell under water.
☑ All true seals have a balloon-like nasal sac.

Page 27

Start

Finish

Page 28

False! Tusks are found on both males and females, though they are usually smaller on females.

Page 30

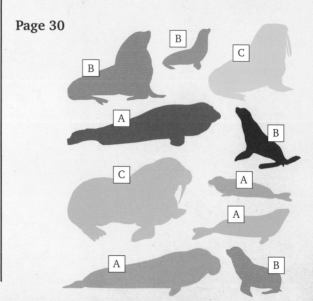

Page 31
A: Pacific B. Arctic C. Atlantic D. Southern E. Indian

Pages 36-38
A: Long-finned pilot whale
B: White-beaked dolphin
C: Hector's dolphin
D: Atlantic spotted dolphin
E: Southern right whale dolphin
F: Irrawaddy dolphin
G: Hourglass dolphin
H: Risso's dolphin
I: Short-beaked common dolphin
J: Indo-Pacific humpbacked dolphin

Page 39

Pages 42-43
A: Finless porpoise   D: Spectacled porpoise
B: Dall's porpoise   E: Burmeister's porpoise
C: Vaquita porpoise   F: Harbour porpoise

Page 46

Page 47
1. ninety minutes
2. two thousand
3. Cachalot

Page 49

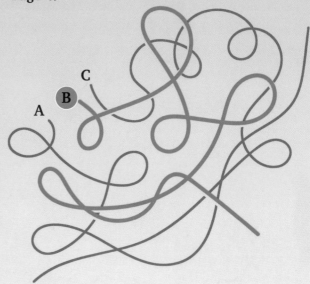

Page 53
1. Beluga 2. white 3. Blue whale

Page 55
Elephant

Page 56
You can make more than 500 words using the letters in "marine mammals"! Here are a handful of possibilities. Did you get any of these?

alarms	learn	mine	sail	snail
aliens	mailman	name	sea	snarl
animal	males	near	seam	
area	man	rains	sir	
arms	men	real	slime	
email	miles	remains	smile	

Page 61

● = African manatee

● = West Indian manatee

● = Dugong

Page 62

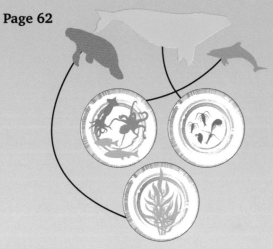

Page 63

A: Bottlenose dolphin
B: Blue whale
C: Right whale
D: Gray whale
E: Humpback whale
F: Sperm whale

Page 71

If you circled all of them, you're right!
A car tire, rubber boot, glass bottles, and even jewelry have all been found in shark bellies.

Page 74

Animal 1: Beluga whale
Animal 2: Sea otter
Animal 3: Dugong
Animal 4: Great white shark
Animal 5: Sea lion

Page 75

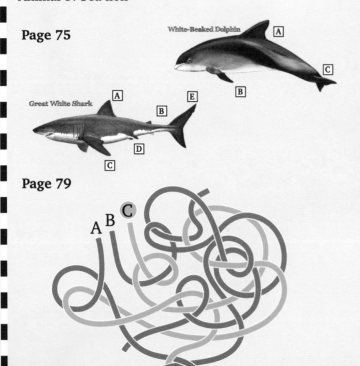

Page 79

Page 87

Page 87

False! Stingrays use their stingers for self-defense. They locate prey using smell and a sensory organ called ampullae of Lorenzini.

Page 89

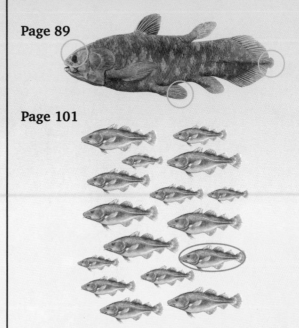

Page 101

Page 110

Page 111

Only five percent of the earth's oceans have been explored.

Page 118

1
2
3
4

Page 128

Page 129

```
C G S U H A Q U C J Z W Z I B A Z A Q S
V W U R E L K M A U G U G D S Z D O F I
P D C M A P W X C E T H P M H F Y V B P
A X K H V H G X S Y I T E H V O W L N H
K Q E S I B K L B Q Q S L G W U O W J O
D Y R I C C E J X N C W T E E J Z D J N
O T S O X V P A N V R G G E B N M P X T
F M E A J A G L K T J F M M B O W I F L
C I Q B X D S W K M G B I L I F N W S W
V O B D J X R J O D L Q B V N H H E W R
U G C H Q I D Y H T U U U T G K M B W M
C H R O M A T O P H O R E S A W Y I O A
V H G V L A W H G O W S J Y E S X M T R
O G I M Y H J A N T D A A K P M R G I N
N Q Q V N N L M T V W J V D N E D K I S
J K C L F L C M G J T E N T A C L E U Y
M A N T L E Y X U M Q D Q R O I Q E J P
Q G B W D S Q W X D I T F P S W Z H M C
G Y C N L G X S H W W Q K V T H K B U P
T K B U E T R A D U L A L G N S E Y I V
```

Page 132

The giant squid is about as long as a school bus and sometimes even longer!

Page 135

Animal 1: Octopus
Animal 2: Clownfish
Animal 3: Eel
Animal 4: Hammerhead shark

Page 143

⬤ = Great cormorant

⬤ = Magnificent frigatebird

⬤ = Flightless cormorant

Pages 144-145

A: Emperor penguin
B: King penguin
C: Chinstrap penguin
D: Northern rockhopper penguin
E: Galapagos penguin
F: Gentoo penguin

Page 149

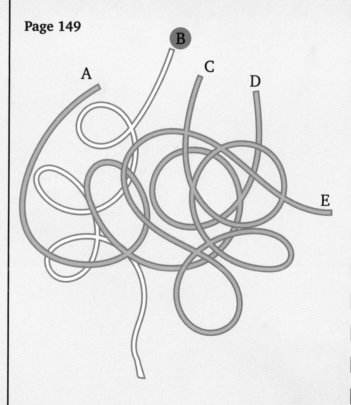

A
B
C
D
E

Glossary

Baleen plates: Flexible material growing from the upper jaw of baleen whales used to filter small animals from the water.

Bio sonar: Also called echolocation; the process of locating objects by sensing reflected echos.

Blowhole: A hole on top of the heads of whales, dolphins, and other cetaceans used to breathe.

Cartilaginous: Made of cartilage, a strong but flexible material.

Chromatophores: Cells or groups of cells that contain pigment used to change color or pattern, found in many cephalopods.

Class: A biological classification of animals or organisms that share the same common attributes. This classification falls between Phylum and Order. For the complete list of animal classification, see page 5.

Ecosystem: A community of organisms and their environment.

Family: A biological classification of animals or organisms that have similar attributes. This classification falls between Order and Genus. For the complete list of animal classification, see page 5.

Fluke: In biology, the tail of cetaceans including whales, dolphins, and porpoises.

Food web: A system of interlaced food chains within an ecological community.

Genus: A biological classification of animals or organisms that share very similar attributes or are closely related. This classification falls between Family and Species.

Gular pouch: A large pouch underneath the lower jaw in marine birds used for catching fish.

Hyponome: A siphon found in mollusks including cephalopods used for propulsion.

Kingdom: The highest rank of biological classification of living organisms. There are five kingdoms representing all living things.

Melon: In zoology, an organ found on the forehead of toothed whales used for vocalizations and bio sonar.

Order: A biological classification of animals or organisms that share attributes or traits. This classification falls between Class and Family.

Phylum: A broad biological classification of animals or organisms that share attributes. This classification falls between Kingdom and Class.

Phytoplankton: Microscopic marine plants.

Pinniped: A group of carnivorous marine mammals including seals and the walrus.

Plankton: Small organisms drifting in both ocean and fresh water.

Rostrum: In zoology, a projection from the head that forms a stiff snout.

Species: The basic biological classification of animals or organisms that share the same attributes.

Suborder: A biological classification of animals or organisms that share similar attributes or traits. This classification falls between Order and Family.

Swim bladder: A gas-filled organ found in many fish species used to control buoyancy.

Trophic levels: The levels in which energy travels in a food chain (or food web) from basic organisms to top predators through consumption.

Zooplankton: Plankton consisting of small animals.

Stickers

Award Stickers

Thickest Fur

Smartest

Heaviest Brain

Longest Tusk

Largest Animal

Largest Baleen Plates

Largest Fish

Largest Ray

Heaviest Bony Fish

Longest Bony Fish

Smartest Invertebrate

Largest Wingspan

Strongest Bite

Page 74

Sea Otter

Dugong

Great White Shark

Beluga Whale

Sea Lion

Page 135

Clownfish

Hammerhead
Shark

Eel

Octopus

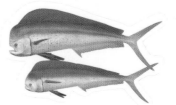